THE
WARWICK TODD
DIARIES

By the same author...

A Year at the Crease
Another Year at the Crease
22 Hard Yards
The Australian Book of Erotic Cricket Stories

THE
WARWICK TODD
DIARIES

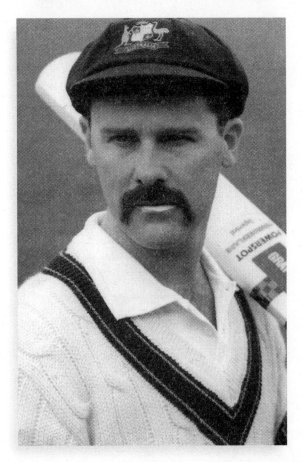

AS TOLD TO TOM GLEISNER

ABC
BOOKS

Warwick Todd is proud to be associated with

THE FINE PINE FURNITURE CENTRE

He denies any association with:

QUICKGROW OSTRICH ENTERPRISES; UNCLE RON'S HOME FOR BOYS;
J. GOLDSTEIN INVESTMENT SERVICES; POP FRUITS THE EXPLODING BUBBLE GUM;
THE SUNSHINE BUILDING SOCIETY; BLITZER'S NIGHTCLUB

Published by ABC Books for the
AUSTRALIAN BROADCASTING CORPORATION
GPO Box 9994 Sydney NSW 2001

Copyright © Tom Gleisner 1997

First published 1997

National Library of Australia
Cataloguing-in-Publication entry

Gleisner, Tom, 1962-   .
The Warwick Todd Diaries: as told to Tom Gleisner.

ISBN 0 7333 0578 4.

1. Cricket – Humor. I. Australian Broadcasting
Corporation. II. Title.

796.3580207

Designed/typeset by Deborah Brash/Brash Design Pty Ltd
Set in 11.5/17 pt Stone Informal
Colour separations by HiTech Graphics, Melbourne
Printed and bound in Australia by
Australian Print Group, Maryborough, Victoria

5 4 3 2 1

ACKNOWLEDGMENTS

Special thanks, plus my undying respect and admiration to every member of the Aussie touring squad who has worn the baggy green cap with pride and guts.

Thanks also to AB for doing me the honour of writing the foreword.

And thanks to Billy Pinnell for the many weeks he put into compiling a comprehensive list of Ashes tour statistics — sorry there wasn't room to put any of them in.

And finally, the Australian Cricket Board — go and get stuffed.

Tom Gleisner would like to thank

Ron Steiner, Tony Dodemaide, Deb Choate, Susannah Mott, Nikki Hamilton, Steven Clode, Kitty Stuckey, Carrie Kennedy, Ben Morieson, Kate Evans, plus my fellow Working Dogs Michael Hirsh, Rob Sitch, Santo Cilauro and Jane Kennedy.

Editor Stuart Neal; designer Deb Brash; original photographs by David Lott; additional photographs by Mark Ray, Trent Parke, Patrick Eagar, Australian Picture Library and Action Photographics; photo imaging by Robert Taylor.

Photographic Credits

All photographs taken by David Lott except the following as credited: Australian Picture Library pages 8 (Putland), 25 (Mason), 52 (Mann), 54 (Mason), 77; Mark Ray pages 12, 23, 30, 59, 85, 102; Patrick Eagar pages 40 (left), 73, 97, 100; Trent Parke pages 49, 137, 146, 148.

Colour insert #1: Page 1 (top left & right) Patrick Eagar; (bottom) David Lott. **Page 2** (top left & right) David Lott; (bottom) Action Photographics/Cox. **Page 3** (top left) Patrick Eagar; (top right) David Lott; (bottom) Action Photographics/Cox. **Page 4** Patrick Eagar.

Colour insert #2: Page 1 (top) David Lott; (bottom) Patrick Eagar. **Pages 2,3 & 4** David Lott.

Colour Insert #3: Page 1 David Lott. **Page 2** Patrick Eagar. **Page 3** (top) Patrick Eagar; (bottom) David Lott. **Page 4** Action Photographics/Cox.

Illustration on page 10 by Paul Stanish.

To my darling wife Ros,
who not only put up with me being
away on tour for months at a time,
but actively encouraged it

When I first started compiling this Ashes diary
I asked noted journalist
Robert 'Robbo' McKean to provide a short poem...

Ballad of a Champion

With an eye as sharp as an eagle
And a heart like old Phar Lap
He's a thorough champion
Who wears the Aussie cap.
Even on a hundred
He'll still find something more
Our green and gold achiever
The mighty Steven Waugh.

I'd like to thank Robbo for his contribution.
Next time I'll make myself a little clearer.

FOREWORD

It gives me great pride to write this foreword to Warwick Todd's book. I first met Toddy during a Shield game in '85. As a new player he naturally copped a fair bit of curry from the boys in close. His ears must have been red raw, but he said nothing until he got to fifty, at which point he turned 'round to the slips cordon and said something I'll never forget; 'Go f#*k yourselves!' He earnt a lot of respect that day.

Since that day I've had the privilege of captaining Toddy for many years and I've never seen that aggressive on-field demeanour wane once. Sure, it's got him into hot water, but everyone in the Australian team knew that if his mouth wasn't doing the talking his bat would.

I guess one incident sums up Toddy. It was '93, we were playing a county match against Kent and the crowd were really getting stuck into us. Toddy was on strike and copping heaps from the small but vocal crowd when one voice rang out; 'You're a homosexual Todd!'. We all thought he was gonna lose it. You couldn't have thought of a worse insult to go to the heart of a man. But the game was at a delicate stage and the big fella just turned his back and played on. We knew he was hurtin' inside but there was a job to be done. Toddy went on to make 82 not out and steer us to victory. I think we all learnt a lesson that day.

Whether it's out on the paddock, behind the bar, on international plane flights or in disciplinary hearings before the ICC Toddy never gives an inch. It would be safe to say no one has prized his baggy green cap with more guts and determination than Warwick Todd. And whenever I see an oversized pair of Bolle wrap-around sunglasses, facial hair and a cocky sneer out at the crease I'll know that Australia is in good hands.

Good on ya' Toddy.

AB, 1997

PREFACE

Cricket's a funny game. If you'd have told me when I was a kid that one day I'd be taking guard for Australia I'd say you were (expletive deleted) fuckin' mad. And if you'd told me I'd be unceremoniously dumped from the Aussie team some 20 years later at the peak of my career, I'd have said much the same thing, only louder. Yet the 1997 Ashes campaign was to be my last international tour as an Australian cricketer. It was during this series I was dropped, dumped by an administration so out of touch with the game it wouldn't know a full toss from a flipper. I'm not bitter. I wouldn't give those bureaucratic bastards in the ACB the pleasure of being bitter. And you know what? I don't regret a minute of my first-class career. Cricket's been good to me — no question. As an international player I've travelled the world, seen some amazing places, dined with royalty and showbiz stars alike. I count Leo Sayer as a personal friend. None of this would have happened if I'd never donned the baggy green and gold — the finest tracky daks in the world...

I count Leo Sayer as a personal friend.

This humourous view of my attitude towards Indian umpires caused quite a few chuckles on the team bus. I bought the original and it now takes pride of place on the pool room wall.

INTRODUCTION

I'll be straight with you. When the folks at ABC Books first asked me to put together this diary, I was hesitant. To be honest, modesty got the better of me. Sure, I'm a brilliant cricketer, a dashing stroke-player with a sharp eye and reflexes to match, who's carved out a place for himself in the international arena with flair and style. But a writer? It's not really my caper. But then I got to thinking. What if we all took that attitude? What if everyone who's ever played first-class cricket decided they weren't going to complete an autobiography? Or a tour diary? Or a book of humorous yarns? Or a series of disjointed anecdotes cobbled together by a ghost writer? Can you imagine that? A world without cricketers producing cricket books. It's hard to get your head around. But chew on this statistic: more than 20 per cent of the current Australian Test team are yet to release a publication. I'm not calling it irresponsible, but it does put the pressure on the rest of us.

And so this book. Now don't expect poetry here, folks. I ain't no William Wordsmith. And don't start looking for 'dirt' either. I'm not about to start bagging other players here. (See Days 18, 23, 42–48, and 56.) Nor am I gonna get all personal, lifting the lid on my love life or talking about my first sexual encounter. That would be unfair to the person involved. He's got a family. And parishioners. But I do promise this. A unique glimpse behind the scenes of an Ashes campaign from someone who was there. Now I know the old rule 'what happens on tour, stays on tour', and I've always adhered to it. That was until the folks at ABC Books offered me the advance. So strap yourself in folks, it's time to take off...

Picture the scene. The cream of Aussie cricket gathered at Sydney airport, trying to look inconspicuous in our green pin-striped blazers, dark pants and wraparound sunglasses.

Saying goodbye to family and loved ones is never easy. The tears, the hugs, the long lingering kisses — I'm glad Ros and the kids weren't there to witness it all.

The 17-member squad was in a relaxed mood, chatting and sipping Coke for the benefit of our sponsor. Speaking of Coke, as usual they'd bombarded us the day before at the pre-tour fit-out with all manner of merchandise: T-shirts, caps, pants, drink bottles. Far more than anyone could possibly take away with them, so that afternoon I did the right thing and popped into the Sydney Children's Hospital with a giant bag full of goodies. Managed to sell most of them before lunch.

Saying goodbye to loved ones is never easy, especially to someone you've only just met in the airport cocktail lounge.

There were quite a few members of the press at the airport and as usual most of the attention was directed at our glamour boy, the so-called 'Sheik of Tweak', Shane 'Warney' Warne. Now I know for a fact that certain members of the Australian team have been getting a little shirty with Warney and all the interest he receives. I've even heard it suggested that he goes out of his way to attract media attention. (You don't think his wife being due to give birth six weeks into the tour wasn't *planned*?) As for me, I say 'good luck to him'. As a senior player I've had more than enough of the media spotlight. If anything, I yearn for the day when the name WARWICK TODD ceases to attract the attention it does.

Looking around the departure lounge there are a few old faces from the 1993 Ashes campaign missing. Most notably, our former skipper Allan Border. My clearest memory of AB from that last England tour was the night we retained the Ashes at Headingley. We just about tore the dressingroom apart with singing and drinking. There was beer flowing everywhere. I went over to AB and said, 'We did it, eh?' AB just grunted and went off to sit by himself. I'd never seen him so happy.

Suddenly we heard our boarding call — time to say '*oh revoir* Australia!'.

As anyone who has ever travelled on a long international flight knows, it's pretty easy to get bored and understandably a few quiet drinks were consumed to help pass the time. This led to several minor 'incidents' breaking out, including a couple of good-natured scuffles, a full-on food fight and an impromptu game of touch footy. But eventually the captain's voice was heard, announcing we were about to take off, and everyone resumed their seats ready for the long trip ahead.

AB after our historic Ashes win in 1993. I've never seen him so happy.

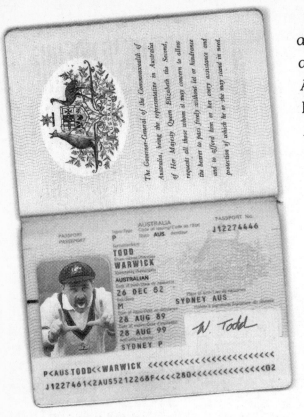

Soon after take-off our meal arrived: steak in a mustard sauce, accompanied by some fine Australian wine. Now I know a lot of people hear stories about Aussie cricketers playing up on board flights but I'm pleased to say that sort of behaviour is all a thing of the past. Today's Test cricketer is not only a professional athlete but also an ambassador for his country and, though it may not make for great reading, I have to say our flight passed without incident. Or at least, what I can remember of it did. Shortly after dinner I fell asleep and the next thing I recall was coming off the plane at Hong Kong airport in a luggage trolley.

By the time we checked in at the Salisbury Hotel I'd recovered sufficiently from the flight (according to Tugga I was as 'jet-lagged as a newt') and managed to join the team for dinner. Strolling to the restaurant you really got a taste of what an extraordinary place Hong Kong is. It's packed with people. There are roadside stalls offering every sort of exotic food imaginable, insane rickshaw drivers, hawkers, and of course hundreds of beggars. Young kids, cripples, mothers with babies — it's something you get used to ignoring in India or Pakistan, but not in a developed country like Hong Kong. A few of the younger guys wanted to give them money but I explained that this only encouraged people to keep begging. Better to maintain a strict policy of giving nothing. It's the same principle back home with the Red Shield Appeal. If you say 'yes' to one Salvo they'll be back knocking on your door the next year, guaranteed.

**OFFICIAL REPORT OF CATHAY PACIFIC FLIGHT 100
SENIOR PURSER**

- Safety handle prised from the emergency door.
- Stewardess's jacket souvenired by a member of touring party.
- Bottles and cans thrown around the cabin.
- Public address system commandeered by a person claiming to be Captain Todd, who informed passengers aircraft engines were 'on fire and rooted'.
- Constant homophobic remarks made in presence of male cabin crew.
- Contents of dinner trays hurled about the cabin, staining seats, carpet and bulkhead.
- Duty-free liquor consumed.
- Passenger Todd attempted to open the emergency door and 'get off the bus'.

After a decent meal (Chinese, of course) we wandered back to the Salisbury. Even though it was late the streets were still full. Hong Kong is certainly a city of contrasts. You'd walk past a luxury shopping complex, turn a corner, and there'd be a run-down squatters camp with people urinating against a wall. Why Ponts and BJ couldn't have waited until we got back to the hotel I'll never know.

Today's match, against a Rest of the World XI, is not part of the official Ashes program but we agreed to play because it was a good way of promoting cricket internationally. And they were offering two and a half grand per player.

It was a good game which Australia won by four wickets, the only sour note being Tubs' failure yet again with the bat. Mark's been suffering from a real form slump for the past six months and all us players feel for him. In my opinion he's getting too much advice from people offering instant remedies. It's time Tubs looked within, for that's where the answer lies. And he should adjust his grip.

Back to the airport for a late-night flight to London. I tell you, one man who has his work cut out on this tour will be our scorer Mike Walsh. In addition to scoring, his job is to handle our baggage, making sure every time we check in and out of a hotel there are 55 suitcases. And that's just Warney's gear. There's the rest of the team's bags to look after as well.

DAY 1 MAY 13

Touchdown, Heathrow airport, 5.50 am. After so long in the air it was good to reach the comfort of the Westbury Hotel in London. Our tour manager Alan 'Crommo' Crompton started calling out room allocations. It's standard policy to change room-mates on a fairly regular basis, in order to prevent any two players getting overly friendly and dragging the good name of Australian cricket into the mud. (The less said about the 1996 tour of India, the better.) But even so, you'll keep the same 'roomie' for a few weeks so this is a pretty important moment. There's a few blokes you want to avoid — guys like Ian Healy, who's a top fella but a complete neatness freak. He's the sort of person who thinks nothing of changing his jocks three times a week. Heals also tends to talk in his sleep, which can be a bit annoying, especially as the only thing he ever says is 'bowled Warney'.

Another 'dubious' roomie would be our coach Geoff Marsh. Guys who played with Swampy back in the 1980s swear they've woken up in the early hours of the morning to find him buck naked in front of a mirror with a bat practising his strokes. Not a pretty sight, especially his sweep shot. Thankfully for all concerned our coach now gets a room (and mirror) to himself.

In the end I scored Michael 'Slats' Slater, the young New South Welshman who I personally believe is going to be one of the finest batsmen this country has ever produced.

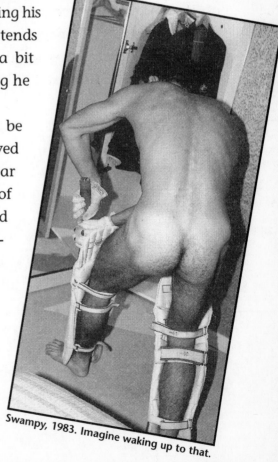

Swampy, 1983. Imagine waking up to that.

Amazingly, all our luggage arrived in one piece and it was time to unpack. Within seconds there were cries of outrage coming from just about every room. Seems that someone had removed all Mark 'Junior' Waugh's jocks and socks from his kitbag. Meanwhile Greg 'Blewie' Blewett was holding up two house-bricks that had been added to his bag — no wonder he'd been struggling with it! And the stench emanating from Glenn 'Pigeon' McGrath's coffin could only mean one thing; the old prawn heads in the batting gloves trick. (Had to be Michael 'Bev' Bevan — still smarting from the time Pigeon super-glued his passport together.)

This sort of good-natured tomfoolery is an essential part of any Aussie touring team. Inconveniencing, embarrassing or just plain hurting each other provides a great way of lifting team morale, and every squad has its resident practical joker. On the 1993 Ashes tour of England it was Merv Hughes, and I think everyone was sorry he wouldn't be joining us on this campaign. Merv was a great fast bowler, fiercely competitive with a heart as big as an ox. Unfortunately, so is the rest of his body these days and he didn't quite make the team.

Despite being totally jet-lagged, experience taught us the most sensible thing to do was to hang out until evening before giving in to the body's natural temptation to start drinking.

At 6.00 pm a team meeting was called, with various 'housekeeping' issues sorted out: allowances, security, who's growing beards etc. Crommo kicked things off by announcing he'd like to say a few words; 45 minutes later he was still going.

After dinner a few of us hit the hotel bar for a couple of quiet refreshments before calling it quits around 11.00, and heading back to our rooms where we got changed, jumped in a cab, and hit the town. Hello, London!

DAY 2 MAY 14

The day dawned to an overcast sky, a familiar sight in England. Upon coming down to breakfast things started looking even bleaker.

Bloody journalists! We had an article from the *Australian* faxed to us this morning that suggested the team had 'misbehaved' on the flight over from Sydney. I honestly slept through most of the trip but asking round it did emerge that there were a few 'incidents'. A couple of the guys (who shall remain nameless), apparently had one or ten too many and pinched a hostie's jacket. Someone else commandeered a wheelchair belonging to a passenger in business class and several seats were apparently damaged during a card game that got a little out of hand. On top of this the chief purser was sprayed with beer when he asked a couple of the boys to stop smoking. Naturally the press focused on the negative aspect of all this, which is just typical. Australian touring sides have always had to put up with this sort of thing. Mind you, it's not just the Aussie journos, the Poms are worse.

I can remember our last Ashes tour (or bits of it) when we were playing Lancashire and this outrageous article opposite appeared in the *Manchester Evening News*.

> ...the appalling behaviour did not stop there. According to hotel management numerous glasses were broken, Australian players urinated in a fountain, several exotic fish in the lobby aquarium were poisoned, a revolving door was removed from its hinges and a naked woman was chased along a corridor on the mezzanine level.

At the time, team management instructed us players to make no comment on the article but now, several years on, I think I can reveal just how inaccurate the report actually was. It may come as a bit of a bombshell to the Fleet Street scribes, but several of the fish were already dead! Still, never let the truth get in the way of a good story, eh fellas?

After breakfast we had a light training run and I was pleased to find my knee held up well. My left knee has been my Achilles heel for the past few seasons, ever since I tore it during the Boxing Day Test in 1995.

According to my specialist Mr Michael 'Benno' Bennings, I'd suffered 'tearing to the cruciate ligaments of the knee and patella, shredding of medial tendon and lateral meniscus and severe damage to gristle overlying the femur'. To be honest, I don't even remember falling off the bar but we were celebrating pretty hard. When they opened me up the medicos also removed a cyst they described as being 'the size of a golf ball'. Tests from the pathology lab a few days later revealed it was a golf ball, courtesy of a wayward shot I copped during a social match in Perth. Since then I've undergone a complete knee reconstruction, months of physio and six days in a de-tox centre, but even now, two years later, the knee can still get a little stiff.

Back at the hotel there was a team meeting followed by free time. I know how easy it is for young players touring England for the first time to be led astray, so I decided to take a few of the junior boys — Dizzy, Ponts, Gilly — aside and explain the importance of training and discipline over a few beers. I then elaborated on the point at several nightclubs before drumming it home at the hotel bar. By the time they staggered up to their rooms round 4.30 am I think I'd made it clear what an Ashes tour is all about.

Arriving back in my room I discovered Slats was asleep which was too good an opportunity to miss. I grabbed Heals (practical joker extraordinaire) and together we rigged up a bucket of water over Slats' bed, skilfully designed to tip over at the exact moment we pushed it. Which we then did. Slats woke up coughing and spluttering, screaming blue murder. That'll teach him not to go to bed before midnight!

DAY 3 | MAY 15 | **Australia vs. Duke of Norfolk XI**

An early morning wake-up call saw us climbing bleary-eyed onto the bus at 7.30 am for the trip to Sussex.

Our first game in England, a one-dayer against the Duke of Norfolk's XI was to be played at Arundel Castle. The castle is about 500 years old which coincidentally is the average age of the players in the Duke of Norfolk team.

It was a good opening match, marred by only one incident. I was on 26, facing up to their captain John Emburey when he got one to nip back a little. I was well forward when it clipped the top of my pad and thought nothing of it as the ball sailed through to their keeper. Imagine my surprise then when the entire team goes up, followed by the umpire's finger. Arguably the worst caught behind decision in

I simply glanced back down the wicket at the umpire.

the history of cricket. Of course, I'm a professional, not to mention an ambassador for my country, and I copped the decision sweet. I simply glanced back down the wicket at the umpire to let my feelings be known and then, four or five minutes later, walked off the field.

We went on to win the match comfortably, and as usual with a game of this nature there were a few relaxing drinks with the opposing team at the end of the day. I must admit, I'm starting to develop quite a taste for the local brews although Slats poured me a shocker; warm and flat, he said it was a traditional English ale. If you'll pardon the French, it tasted like piss. Turned out it was. I swear I'm gonna get him back.

Back at the hotel I decided to give Ros a ring, just to see how she's getting on. To be honest, I worry about leaving her home alone with two kids but she sounded quite cheery when she picked up the phone. Turns out my old mate from district cricket days, Garry Beckman, has just arrived unexpectedly from interstate. I haven't seen Gazza in years, he always seems to be in town when I'm off touring, but just knowing he's about to keep an eye on Ros makes me feel a lot better.

After a quick shower back at the hotel it was off to an official function. These events — drinks, dinners, quiz nights etc. — are generally put on by our sponsor and every player is expected to attend his fair share. In 1993 this wasn't too hard as our tour sponsor was XXXX. This time round it's Coke and I think I'm going to be struggling.

DAY 4 MAY 16

Woke this morning to the sound of rain. Opened my eyes and discovered the fire sprinklers had been set off. How Junior managed to do it without waking Slats or me is a mystery, but you've got to hand it to him.

Naturally the Pommy press were up to their old tricks, focusing on the negative side of our victory yesterday, questioning my sportsmanship in not *sprinting* off the field the moment I was allegedly 'dismissed'.

Many of us Aussies were lucky enough to be joined on tour by family and loved ones.
Anticlockwise from top: Warney and his dad, Tugga and his mum and my uncle Colin Todd.

I barely had time to shove a souvenir bathrobe in my bag before it was onto the bus for our trip to Northamptonshire. By now positions on the bus are just about set, with the front reserved for non-smokers. This leaves the other 14 of us plenty of room down the back.

The bus trip passed quickly and after settling in at the Swallow Hotel, Swampy called a pretty serious training session. He's a top bloke Geoff Marsh and I get on well with him, which is more than can be said for his predecessor. It's no secret that Bob Simpson and I never really saw eye-to-eye. Although I should stress he did contribute a lot to the Australian team. Before Simmo took over as coach in 1986 we lacked direction. But after he arrived the team all became focused on the one goal. Getting rid of him.

My main gripe with Simmo was the fact he acted as both coach and selector. Put yourself in the position of a player with a minor technical problem and ask yourself if you would go to the coach for advice if he was also a selector and the side was being chosen that night? This exact dilemma presented itself to me on the eve of the first Test against England here in 1993 when, after a lengthy session in the nets, I discovered a footwork problem. Should I tell Simmo? Should I not? In the end I decided yes, and pointed out to him just how badly Matt Hayden was handling the leg-spin bowling. Next thing I knew — Hulkster is carrying the drinks. Not fair, is it?

After the team meeting tonight we dined at a local steakhouse. Some of the guys then wanted to check out the local pubs but with an important game the next day Tubs put his foot down and said 'no'. So we ended up getting a few takeaways from an off-licence and kicking on back at the hotel.

DAY 5 MAY 17

**Australia vs.
Northamptonshire**

Woke this morning to the sight of dull grey. A typical English sky. Took me a few minutes to realise I was lying face down on the carpet, halfway between the bedroom and the dunny. To make matters worse, it wasn't even my room. Eventually I made it down to breakfast where things deteriorated further. It wasn't my hotel. If there are any young aspiring batsmen reading this book, take a tip from me — never mix Kahlua and Midori.

I eventually managed to get a flight back from Dublin (not easy without pants), and made it to the ground just in time for the toss.

My main memory of our clash with Northamptonshire is the wild scenes in the Australian dressing-room. Cold Chisel blasting from the CD player, Tubs standing on the physio's bench shouting 'Aussie, Aussie, Aussie', Heals belting out 'Under the Southern Cross' and everyone downing beer like it's going out of fashion. It was a pity the

The Australian dressing-room at lunch.

You should have heard the laughs.

party had to end but you only get 40 minutes for lunch and we still had to bowl.

The rain-shortened match was marred by only one incident late in the game when one of their openers, Malachy Loye, was attempting to take a quick single and collided heavily with yours truly. We both hit the ground awkwardly and I shuddered as I heard the all-too-familiar sound of ligaments tearing. Fortunately there was a happy ending — it was his knee not mine, and we went on to win the game comfortably while he was carted off on a stretcher.

Among the other plusses, Tubs scored 76 while Kaspa bowled with accuracy and rhythm, two of a bowler's greatest assets. I guess a few wickets would be nice as well.

After the game we all stayed to enjoy a few quiet drinks with the Northants boys. This social side to cricket is, in my opinion, also a valuable part of the game, a chance for a young local team to sit down and learn a thing or two from players they've just been comprehensively thrashed by.

Another official function tonight, the MCC welcoming dinner. Started out a bit stuffy with a lot of boring speeches but after dinner I decided to lighten things up by unveiling a comedy character I came up with during the World Cup. With the aid of a turban (made from a towel) and a bit of shoe polish I entered the dining room as Pakistani cricketer Punjabber Mahandupmabum. Well, you should have heard the laughs. I couldn't actually hear any but I figured the turban must have been blocking my ears. I've got a sneaking suspicion we could be hearing quite a bit more from Punjabber.

DAY 6 | MAY 18 | Australia vs. Worcestershire

Outside the hotel this morning several members of the squad were required to pose for a photo beside two brand-new Peugots. Peugot are the team's official car sponsor for the tour and as they're supplying these vehicles for the players' use we were happy to oblige. (The photo was later to prove very useful in the insurance claim we had to make after both cars were driven off a pier in Southampton.)

Travelling to the ground this morning the bus made a brief detour in order for us to visit Stonehenge, one of England's most famous landmarks. It was kind of eerie standing there between the giant stone blocks, built by Druids hundreds of years ago. According to the guidebook, many of the larger blocks (called 'sarsen stones') have ancient carvings on them dating from the dawn of time. We looked pretty closely but all we could find was one carving: 'Merv was here 1993'. Some of the fellas wanted to add their names but we felt that given Merv Hughes is no longer in the side it would almost amount to desecration.

The match today was a good one, marred by only one unfortunate incident (or two, if you count the fact we lost). It involved myself and a rather abusive English spectator who lunged at me as I was leaving the

field after a well-compiled 27. Instinctively I raised my bat, more out of self-defence than any desire to hit him and, to my surprise, I hit him. Naturally there was a fair amount of ill-informed comment in the papers, seeing as the entire sequence had been captured by some photographer. I even read calls for me to be banned from international cricket! Let me put the incident to rest once and for all. Not only was I acting in self-defence, if you look closely at the photos you'll see I was actually off the playing field when the altercation took place, therefore removing it from ICC jurisdiction and making it a private matter between me and the deceased.

DAY 7 MAY 19

Another early start, another appalling English breakfast. Is there anything these people don't serve with peas? Thank God our team manager Crommo had the foresight to bring over two massive jars of Vegemite. One was on the table this morning, the other has been left (minus its lid) in Glenn McGrath's kitbag. I can't wait to see him when he opens it and discovers his 'whites'.

During the bus trip to Durham in the northeast of England Swampy gave us a real blast over yesterday's loss, issuing the entire team with a get-tough order. He sounded pretty serious so as soon as we'd checked into the Royal Country Hotel I hit the gym for a massage, sauna and spa. I even considered a haircut but didn't want to overdo things.

Tomorrow we play Durham and although they're not a top county side, at the team meeting tonight both Tubs and Swampy spoke about the importance of not becoming complacent, of keeping up the intensity. It was a great speech and I just wish more of the players had been there to hear it, but with Junior and Warney's poker school running upstairs, who could blame them?

DAY 8 MAY 20

Australia vs. Durham

Up early this morning and I put another call through to Ros, hoping to catch her before she hit the sack, but I must have got the wrong number. Some bloke answered, then we were disconnected.

Unfortunately it was raining heavily outside and today's match, against former Australian David 'Boonie' Boon's county Durham, had to be postponed. This is a real blow as it's robbed the team of a valuable

Boonie on the outfield at Durham.

and much-needed chance to drink with a recent Aussie legend.

After lunch Slats was keen to hit the gym but with my knee still a little sore I decided to rest it, against the hotel bar. He's a good kid Slats, and it's great to see him back in the national side. Why he was ever dropped in the first place is questionable — I guess a few people may have been put off by his flamboyant manner, since he's certainly not one for hiding his emotions! I can remember Slats at Lord's in 1993 executing a perfect cover drive then jumping up and down, punching the air and kissing the Aussie badge on his helmet. And this was during a net practice session.

At the team meeting tonight Greg Blewett dropped an absolute bombshell by announcing he no longer wants to be known as Blewie.

A nickname subcommittee was immediately formed to come up with some acceptable alternatives but I don't like his chances. Once you've been given a nickname by the boys you can't just up and change it. I'm Toddy, our captain's Tubs (or Tubby, if you're a senior player). Sure, nicknames may not always be flattering; back in his Shield days Heals was known as 'Sav', short for saveloy, the rather *small* sausage. I don't think I need to say any more.*

* It was a reference to his penis.

DAY 9 MAY 21

Tomorrow's the big day — our first one-day international clash at Headingley. A lot has been written over the years about the one-day game: is it as good as Test cricket? Do the players enjoy it? Are the games 'rigged'? And so on. On that last point I can offer an unconditional 'no!'. Can you imagine an Aussie or English player deliberately throwing a game? A West Indian or Kiwi batsman chucking in their wicket to affect the result? A Paki bowler bending the rules for some financial inducement? Okay, that last one *could* happen, but I can assure you — there's no way an Aussie would ever be involved.

I guess one of the main criticisms levelled at the one-day game in Australia involves the crowds. And it's true, they can often be a little unruly. But that's the nature of the game. It's fast, it's furious and tempers can fray. Things reached a head in Australia during the 1996/97 domestic season when several West Indian players were pelted with bottles at the SCG. It was a disgraceful episode, but thankfully it took place inside the Australian dressing-room and was therefore kept out of the press.

The team for tomorrow's one-day match was announced, with Justin Langer being the unlucky one to miss out. I could tell Lang was pretty devastated but getting overlooked for a team is just part and parcel of first-class cricket. In my opinion Langer's a fine batsman, his biggest shortcoming probably being that he doesn't believe in himself. Cricket is so much a game of confidence and when you start doubting yourself your game inevitably suffers. If Justin Langer wants to become a permanent part of the team he has to — above all else — believe in himself. Only with confidence and the support of his team-mates can he hope to make the Aussie XI. Not that I think he can do it.

Glenn McGrath breaks through at the Oval.

Shane Warne, another Test scalp at Headingley.

Warwick Todd backs a winner at Ascot.

Indicating to Darren Gough where his next ball will end up. Sometimes a bit of cheekiness pays off...

...sometimes it doesn't.

Warney's mad-capped antics often make the headlines, but who was the quick wit pouring beer down the back of his daks? Yep, yours truly. Me. Warwick Todd.

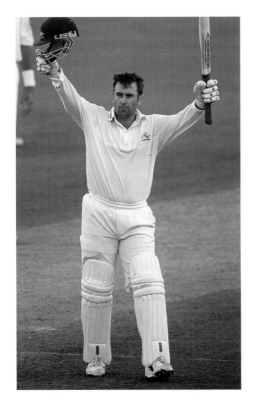

Above: The baggy green and gold.

Left: Reaching three figures is always an emotional time for a batsman. Here, Tubs celebrates reaching double figures.

Swampy's training sessions could often leave you breathless.

Match souvenirs are often hard to come by and you have to be quick. While the boys are celebrating our 4th Test win at Leeds Dizzy takes the opportunity to grab another auction item for his testimonial year.

Heals is a master at sneaking the odd souvenir. Watch him casually make off with a stump at Trent Bridge. Pretty bold when you consider we still had another ten overs to bowl.

DAY 10 | MAY 22 | 1st Texaco Trophy One-Day International, Headingley

The alarm in Room 1523 went off this morning at precisely 6.00. Or, I hope it did, because that's the time I set it for when I snuck into Junior and Bevo's room during the night. Meanwhile, in Room 1524 Slats and I enjoyed a decent sleep-in, wandering down to breakfast at about 8.30.

Most of the guys have got good luck faxes and phone calls from home but I appreciate the fact Ros hasn't tried to make contact. She knows that I like to stay totally focused and rarely communicates on match days. Or pre-match days. Or pretty much any day.

The one-day games here are played in whites, with the traditional red ball. It gives the matches more of a Test feel. The crowd atmosphere is also very different from what you'd find at the SCG or MCG under lights. Most of the spectators are sober, and there's not nearly as much debris hurled onto the arena, but this doesn't detract from the encounter.

Our 12th man was announced during the pre-game warm-up and Julian was something of a surprise choice, considering his excellent form thus far. That a player of BJ's calibre could be omitted indicates just how much better than him the rest of us clearly are.

As predicted, the Poms prepared a very dodgy pitch and, having been sent in, most of us struggled on the slow, seaming wicket. Tubby failed again, managing only 7. Watching him trudge back towards the pavilion I felt a curious mixture of sorrow and regret; sorrow for Tubs getting out and regret that I'd just set fire to his kitbag. (A good practical joke relies heavily on timing and I suspected this was bad timing.)

We managed only 170, a total the Poms had no trouble overhauling. I can tell you, a losing Australian dressing-room is a pretty sombre place to be. Even the CD player was turned down. In addition to being beaten, the game was marred by another incident. And yes, it involved the press again. In a photo taken by the *Daily Mirror* it was alleged you could clearly see me mouthing the phrase 'f#*k off!' to

How could anyone tell what I'm saying here?

English captain Mike Atherton after he was dismissed. Which is total c#*p, with a capital C.R.A.P. For a start, I don't indulge in that sort of unsportsmanlike behaviour, and second, if you look closely at the photo you'll see my mouth is actually obscured by my middle finger pointing up. How could anyone tell what I'm saying here? Yet another beat-up for the British press.

After such a disappointing loss it's often difficult to wind down and get to sleep. Fortunately new room-mates were announced tonight and I got Tugga. No sooner had he begun talking about his district cricket days than I was out like a light.

DAY 11 MAY 23

I overslept this morning and missed the bus but luckily managed to talk Crommo into letting me take one of the team cars back down to London. I enjoy driving overseas, it's no different from Australia except you've got to keep reminding yourself they drive on the opposite side of the road over here. Not that a lot of Poms seem to realise! You wouldn't believe the number of idiots coming head-on at me down the wrong side of the motorway.

At the team meeting tonight manager Allan Crompton reminded us all that the bus would be leaving tomorrow at 8.30. How he managed to stretch this announcement out to 47 minutes remains a mystery. Tubs then spoke about tomorrow's game, saying that to win it was simply a question of batting, bowling and fielding better than the opposition. He's a smart operator Tubs, with a keen insight into the game.

With a few losses under our belt a fair bit has been written in the Aussie press about the Poms deliberately preparing pitches that suit slow, seam bowling. As far as I'm concerned this talk is a distraction, an easy excuse for some people to explain away poor performances. If we want to start winning again we have to stop blaming the pitches and look to the real cause of the problem — the substandard catering. How can anyone go out to play after a lunch of hard-boiled potatoes and pickled herring? Still, we're professional cricketers, and we've simply got to rise above this sort of thing. Enough said.

DAY 12 | MAY 24 | 2nd Texaco Trophy One-Day International, The Oval

The hotel breakfast this morning was inedible. Pre-war porridge, cold toast and baked beans. It's simply not good enough! But let's get back to the cricket.

My main memory of today's second one-day international is the Aussie dressing-room after the match. The ghetto blaster on full bore belting out 'Khe Sahn' and 'Bound for Glory' while the VB flowed and the boys cut loose. Looking round at the wild scenes I couldn't help thinking, Imagine if we'd won.

Despite losing it was a good game, marred by only one incident. You guessed it — the press again. Having tired of probing us with longlenses the good folk at the *Mail on Sunday* today used directional microphones to eavesdrop on the players. For some reason they had one pointed at me for most of the morning, when we were fielding. I came

Imagine if we'd won.

off at the luncheon interval and there's a dozen reporters accusing me of racially abusing Phil DeFreitas! Give us a break, fellas. It's a well-known fact that players often verbalise during a match, but are not necessarily directing remarks towards the opposition. To put it simply, you're speaking to yourself, searching for a better performance. Personally I've lost count of the occasions I've called myself a 'black bastard' or 'Pommy poofta' as a way of spurring myself on. But try explaining that to an English journo.

To our surprise, very few of the home team stayed for drinks after the match. Despite a great victory, most of them were keen to get home. This to me sums up a lot of what is wrong with English cricket today. How can a group of players ever hope to bond as a team if they are not willing to get together and physically write themselves off after a win?

Back at the hotel Tubs dropped a bombshell. He would be standing aside for tomorrow's final match. Looking at Tubby you could tell he was a man under real pressure. Months and months of media speculation as to his future, constant headlines and articles questioning his ability. I don't think he fully realised how bad it had been until last night when I presented them all to him in a scrapbook.

In my opinion, tomorrow is shaping up as a vitally important day for us all. Even though the series is lost it will be a chance to pull ourselves out of a slump and prove to the knockers that we have the commitment and the drive to play winning cricket.

DAY 13 | MAY 25

3rd Texaco Trophy One-Day International, Lord's

I think the importance of one-day matches can be overrated. Okay, we lost today but deep down we all know the Test series is the one we've come here to win. Still, I think everyone's a little shocked at the final scoreline, 3–0. It's a result any bookmaker would have given you 500 to 1 about. Certainly the one I dealt with did.

Looking back, the day began quite well, all of us excited as the team bus pulled into Lord's, the fabled home of international cricket. I remember Bob Simpson once telling me he still gets a thrill every time he enters the place. Mind you, Simmo used to get a thrill out of fielding practice and well-ironed lapels.

Unfortunately our first match at Lord's was marred by an ugly incident involving the cocky English batsman Alec Stewart. I was fielding in slips at the time when he slashed at a Kasprowicz outswinger. The ball snicked his bat, sailed through to the safe hands of Heals and the slips cordon went up as one. 'Not out' came the verdict from the so-called 'independent' umpire at the other end. Well, we're flabbergasted. You could have heard that ball hit Stewart's bat from the outer and the little bastard knew it, but do you think he did the decent thing and walked? Not on your nelly! But we're professional cricketers, we accept the umpire's decision — no matter how shith*#s# — and we settled back in position and waited for Kaspa's next delivery. While Stewart padded up to it those of us fielding close in took the opportunity to utter a few 'pleasantries' in his direction. Nothing too personal, just a few cricket-related comments. Heals asked the obvious question: 'Why didn't you walk?' I added: 'Just like your missus did.' Well, you'd think we'd just called him a child molester (a comment normally reserved for the bloke batting at the other end) instead of making a humorous quip about a potential marital split. Next thing I knew Stewart strutted towards me, waving his arms and then whinged to the square leg umpire who, in an absolute first for Aussie cricket, told us to stop sledging!

Sledging, or the gentle art of verbal harassment, is as much a part of international cricket as ball-tampering and bribery. I've known wicket-keepers in grade competition to be selected for their ability in this area alone. It's a time-honoured tradition for players fielding behind the stumps to engage in a little psychological warfare, trying to put the man at the crease off his game. The only time I've ever had an umpire tell me to stop muttering obscenities to a batsman was during a district final in the mid-1980s. Sure, I was fielding at deep backward square leg at the time and they may have been a little loud, but here's this little twerp of an umpire trying to shut me up. Up at the bowler's end his partner (in more ways than one, but that's another story) is having a go at Kaspa for deliberately scuffing-up the popping crease.

All in all, we didn't have a great day. Eventually calm was restored, Stewart went on to make 79 (24 more than he should have) and the Poms won the match. Predictably, the press focused on the negative aspects of the incident, branding us with the old 'ugly Australian' tag. What these so-called experts sitting up in their air-conditioned commentary boxes don't realise is that whatever happens in the heat of competition on the field, stays on the field. At the end of the day Stewart and I both walked off the field, sat down and enjoyed a beer. Not together, mind you.

DAY 14 | MAY 26

With the bus due to leave at 9.30 it was a rush to have our bags packed. Barely two weeks into the tour and already my suitcase is bulging with souvenirs and tour memorabilia. But there's only so much you can fit in and reluctantly I was forced to leave the Westbury Hotel's TV behind.

On the bus trip to Gloucestershire my mouth was feeling rather dry and Bevo offered me his mouthwash. I took one spray and just about choked on shaving cream.

By the time we arrived at the hotel it was raining quite heavily. Wet weather is part and parcel of touring England and it

✔ RIGHT. A textbook illustration of the shot.

✗ WRONG! Front foot pointing across the line, elbow too high, hands not together. A textbook demonstration of how NOT to play a cover drive.

can greatly restrict a team's options. This afternoon we could only drink at the hotel bar or the pub opposite — any further afield and we'd be drenched.

To make matters worse, new room allocations were handed out. You guessed it — Warney. It's going to be a long three days. To top things off there was a message at the hotel to call my manager Gabe Hirsh back in Australia. Turned out our court action against a Sydney publisher had been unsuccessful. I've never actually sued anyone before but this mob approached me and Steve Waugh a few years back saying they were putting together a cricket coaching manual and would we mind letting them use a photo of each of us batting? Now we're all for giving kids the right coaching advice, after all they are the future of our great game, so naturally we both said 'yes'. But not to the caption they used under my shot.

After a 3–0 series loss everyone was feeling pretty down and a team meeting was called tonight to discuss the obvious question: 'Where do we go from here?' After some quite spirited debate, it was agreed we'd give the local Indian restaurant a go.

DAY 15 MAY 27

**Australia vs.
Gloucestershire — Day 1**

Woke to the sound of heavy rain. I lay there listening to it for about five minutes before realising it was just Warney taking a leak.

A report in the *Guardian* this morning described my innings at Lord's last Sunday as 'languid'. Fortunately for that particular paper I couldn't find a dictionary, but if I had and 'languid' turned out to be as bad as it sounded I would have sued, no question. Of course, cricket writers have a language all of their own but over the years you get wise to their little tricks. If they call you 'pugnacious' it means you're fat. A 'gritty innings' is one where you were dropped at least twice. A 'fierce competitor' tends to mean they think you're a complete psychopath. And watch out if you're called 'a great team man' — you're about to be dropped.

Warney spends a lot of time with his personal fitness advisor.

As it turned out, the rain had cleared overnight allowing today's game to start at the scheduled time. We won the toss and Tubby elected to bat. He's a great team man. I must have been half asleep when we left the hotel because unpacking in the dressing- room I discovered I'd left my inside thigh pad back at the hotel. So of course who do you think gets hit flush on the unprotected thigh by a Mike Smith scorcher? Matthew Elliot — I pinched his pad when he wasn't looking. Herb's also a great team man and it was a pity to see him out soon after for a fairly languid 6.

I came in with the team at 3 for 95 and attempted to move the score along without taking too many risks. I reached 47 in good time and was looking forward to my first half-century of the tour. Imagine my disappointment at being given out lbw off the last ball before tea. Being dismissed at such a crucial time, many thoughts go through your head. Anger, disbelief, dejection, even self-pity. But as a professional cricketer you've got to rise above all this and accept that the blame lies fairly and squarely on one person. The umpire.

The other big disappointment of the day was Tubs, out for a duck in the first over. That, combined with hopelessly inadequate dressing-room facilities (not even the urn was working properly!) made for a tough day with Australia all out for 249.

After the game we had an official engagement — drinks with an equipment sponsor.

DAY 16 | MAY 28

**Australia vs.
Gloucestershire — Day 2**

Woken at 6.30 this morning by a phone call from Australia, some journalist in Perth wanting an interview. Despite the early hour I was willing to oblige — I think the media have an important job to do in promoting the game and it's every cricketer's responsibility to cooperate. But in return I do demand that journos at least ask intelligent questions, unlike the guy this morning. How's this for an opening question? 'Is Shane Warne there?' I mean for God's sake...

I tell you, rooming with Warney is certainly an experience. The guy is on the phone from around dawn doing interviews and reports for the media back home. Not that he's the Lone Ranger there. I have a regular weekly commitment with one of the top radio breakfast shows in Queensland, the *Komedy Klub*, from 4MB-FM Mareeba. It's kind of awe-inspiring sitting in a hotel room in England knowing your voice is being heard right across the Atherton Tablelands.

Gloucestershire resumed this morning at 1 for 55 and we set about bowling them out. Kaspa was the pick of our bowlers, taking three wickets. I've got a lot of time for the big Queenslander, he's a guy who's learnt to play within his ability — which for him is no easy task. Overall it was a good day for Australia, marred only by one unfortunate incident, which naturally the press 'beat up' completely out of proportion. It happened to involve myself and the Gloucestershire opener Nick Trainor. He was on 121 when Pigeon got one to pop up. I dived forward and clutched at the offering, only to see the ball bobble out of my hands as I tumbled towards the turf. On the way down I had another two unsuccessful attempts at securing the prized red cherry before a final grab saw it come to rest on top of my wrist. There were celebrations from all around as Trainor departed the wicket. Little did any of us know that up in the press box a heated debate had erupted over whether the catch was in fact legitimate. A certain 'commentator' (i.e. washed-up hack) even insisted he'd seen the ball hit the ground. It really makes you wonder, doesn't it, how some ageing twit in a BBC blazer tucking into scones 200 metres away can possibly think he has a better view than a man on the spot. The fact is, I'm the first guy to call a batsman back if I believe a catch has not been taken cleanly and a camera may have picked it up. That night I replayed the moment over and over in my sleep, and each time the dream ended the same way. The ball is popped up, I dive forward and take the catch, get named Man of the Match and end up in the dressing-room having sex with the girl from our hotel reception desk. I think I've been away from Ros too long.

With Gloucestershire finally all out for 350 we prepared to leave the ground. Unfortunately, the commentator's opinion had obviously been heard by a few ill-informed idiots in the crowd and their angry feelings were evident. Abusive remarks like 'cheat' and 'lying bastard' were hurled at me as we went off the field. Personally, I'd hate to see the day cricket crowds were separated from the players by soccer-style fences, but if something's not done soon we could well see a Monica Seles-type incident. Not that I'd ever *deliberately* stab a fan, but in the heat of the moment who can tell what might happen?

We resumed our second innings and at stumps were 0 for 43, with Tubs unbeaten on 19. I just know tomorrow's going to be a big one for him.

After the game we had an official engagement — drinks with the tour sponsor.

DAY 17 | MAY 29

Australia vs.
Gloucestershire — Day 3

Arriving at the ground this morning Tubs was met by a representative of the *Mirror*, who presented him with a metre-wide bat. (The *Mirror* would have to be England's most pathetic, trashiest, tabloid newspaper. I don't know why I ever agreed to write a column for them.) Understandably, Tubs was not amused by this 'joke'. Personally, I was appalled by its poor timing; I'd planned on giving him a similar bat but was at least going to wait until the match was over.

Quite a few of the boys got among the runs today, with Elliot and Langer both making centuries. Tubs managed only 30 but he was scratching around with a great deal more confidence. The match ended up in a draw, with Australia at 4 for 354.

A draw was a good result for us, ending a pretty bad run of losses, and the post-match festivities were soon under way. In the general merriment that surrounds a good team performance, it's easy to forget the 12th man, in this case Gilly, who spends the entire match running out with gloves and water. To me these guys are the unsung heroes, working all day for the benefit of a team they're not good enough to be part of.

After the game we had an official engagement — drinks with one of our sponsor's sponsors.

DAY 18 | MAY 30

It was a bleary-eyed bunch of Aussies who crawled onto the team bus this morning for the trip to Derby. The route took us past several McDonald's stores but after so many weeks of junk food we decided to give our bodies a break and ordered our driver to pull in at a KFC.

Several dozen zinger burgers later we pulled into the Breadsall Priory Hotel. After checking in I joined the other guys in the gym. I'm not sure if cricketers of old would have done the same but fitness is such an important factor in international cricket nowadays. We were chatting about this very fact that night over a few beers in the hotel bar.

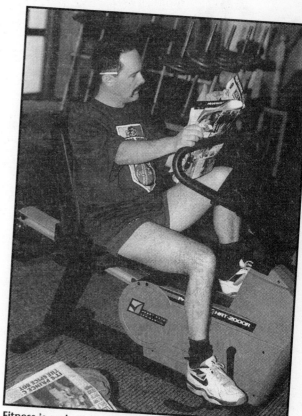

Fitness is such an important factor in international cricket.

Called Ros tonight (local time) for a chat. She was still in bed, despite it being almost 9.30 am back home, and to tell the truth she sounded a little out of breath. The poor girl's obviously shagged out, what with looking after the kids and everything while I'm away. After hanging up I phoned Garry Beckman to see if he'd mind dropping round and checking if Ros was okay but Gazza wasn't home. Ended up leaving a message on his machine. Gazza is a great mate. We played district cricket together. The fact I went on to a sparkling international Test career while he became a roofing contractor has never come between us. And don't let me detract from his cricketing ability. He was a keen competitor. Whenever Gazza was out in the middle you could be guaranteed that runs would flow. Only problem, he would be bowling at the time.

A few of the boys were planning a pub crawl but with a three-day match due to start tomorrow and a slight headache coming on, I decided the best thing for W. Todd would be lying down in a dark room. I got my wish and half an hour later I was stretched out on the bar in some Derby nightclub drinking tequila slammers.

DAY 19 | MAY 31

**Australia vs.
Derbyshire — Day 1**

I woke up before dawn this morning and it felt like the room was on fire. Turned out it was. I don't know how many times I've spoken to Warney about smoking in bed. We eventually managed to put the mattress out and get back to sleep.

Today's game was at the Racecourse Ground in Derby, one of the most uninspiring and coldest cricket venues you could find. Standing in the outfield is a certain recipe for hypothermia — the wind cuts right through you. I actually found myself fantasising about being back in India. (I must be going mad!) India would have to be the hottest country I've ever played in, and without doubt the worst ground is Madras. The heat over there sucks the very oxygen from your body. Of course, it was in Madras that Dean Jones played one of the bravest innings I've ever been privileged to witness. It was in September 1986 and Deano scored 210 over two days in scorching conditions. Towards the end he was having to be carried into the

Madras, India, where Deano scored 210. These women are being paid to search for Tony Grieg's car keys.

dressing-room during breaks where we'd try desperately to pump fluids into him. Eventually Deano could take no more beer and began calling for water. I knew then the situation was serious.

We batted first today, reaching 6 (declared) for 362. Unfortunately Tubby failed again, managing just 5 runs, a result that will no doubt have the press calling even more loudly for his resignation. One of the most outrageous accusations I've read in recent days is that Tubby's poor form is having a 'negative effect' on team morale. Simply not true. If anything, his struggle has brought the rest of us closer together; we've had that many secret crisis meetings behind his back in the last month I've lost count. And let's keep things in perspective; as captain, Tubs still has our 100 per cent respect. It's only as a batsman we think he's a washed-up failure.

DAY 20 | JUNE 1 | Australia vs. Derbyshire — Day 2

More controversy this morning, courtesy of the Pommy press, with a photo of yours truly relaxing yesterday during lunch at the ground plastered across the sports page. According to the smart-arse journalist responsible I was 'caught' drinking Pepsi, our sponsor's main rival. Of course, if this old hack of a reporter had bothered to at least check his facts he would have realised I was not actually 'drinking Pepsi' but rather Pepsi and rum. Puts a rather different complexion on things, doesn't it? Yet again, the English press failed to check their facts.

There was also some controversy on the field this morning with Derbyshire's Chris Adams ruled lbw to Warney and then refusing to leave the pitch! This sort of behaviour has absolutely no place on a cricket field. In my book you've got to accept the umpire's decision. Sometimes it's flawed, incorrect, biased, ill-informed, dubious, questionable, outrageous, open to question, misguided or wrong, and sometimes it's right. That's just part of the game. I believe the Derbyshire committee met over the incident this afternoon and had some stern words to say to Adams. As did our slips cordon yesterday when the little Pommy whinger refused to walk.

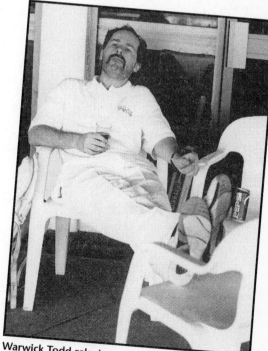

Warwick Todd relaxing at lunch.

Derbyshire declared at 257 shortly after lunch and our openers Herb and Tubs were soon at the crease. With so many batsmen in the squad a fair bit of pressure is starting to emerge for the 11 Test berths up for grabs next week. Looking at things objectively I'd say Justin Langer would have to be my closest rival for a place in the team. Lang's a top bloke and a fine batsman who's scored a heap of runs against pace attacks. I'm told by a *lot* of pretty knowledgeable guys he's a bit suspect against spin bowlers, but as I've not seen much of him playing them in recent times I wouldn't like to comment. Especially as these words might be read by selectors who could be influenced against the man. However, the number of respected commentators who've questioned this *major* flaw in Lang's make-up can't be ignored so let's just state once for the record:

JUSTIN LANGER CANNOT HANDLE SPIN BOWLING

and leave it there.

Our official function tonight, drinks with the local County Cricket Board, was called off to the joy of all. Honestly, night after night standing around drinking is not what a touring Test team needs, and it was a great relief for once to have the night off. To celebrate we all decided to go out drinking.

Justin Langer, a fine batsman but incapable of handling spin bowling.

DAY 21 | JUNE 2 | Australia vs. Derbyshire — Day 3

Another sporting declaration from Tubs this morning left the home team a target of 370, a figure we believed they would struggle to reach. But with our bowling line-up somewhat depleted (you know it must be when Herb is called on to bowl eight overs) the Derbyshire boys looked set to make the runs. Most worrying was the excellent form of yesterday's bad-boy Chris Adams. With no sign of a bowling breakthrough Tubs made a clever adjustment to the field — he brought Tugga into a close-in position where he could offer a few 'pleasantries' to the in-form batsman.

Now let me make this clear, there's a lot more to 'sledging' than just verbal abuse. Often simply chatting with a player can be enough to really put them off their game. Some players hate you talking to them, like Keppler Wessels. It really broke his concentration. Same went for England's old captain Graham Gooch. I discovered on the 1993 tour here that even the friendliest of conversations could really fire him up. All I had to say was stuff like 'How are you going? Looks like being a good game…' and he'd go right off his nut! Looking back on the incident, I'm surprised the switchboard at his hotel ever put my phone call through to his room, seeing as it was 3.00 in the morning, but the technique sure worked. As did Tugga's. Adams was out playing a rash shot shortly after. Unfortunately, he wasn't the only Derby player to get among the runs and the home team managed to win the match with one wicket to spare.

Good news though for Tubby, who made 63. Speaking after the match our captain was quoted as saying 'My feet started moving and I felt my balance coming back'. Footwork and balance are such vital features for an in-form batsman. You only have to look at someone like Boonie who had such a good series here in '93 to see that. One example sticks in my mind. We were partying pretty hard back at the hotel after a win at Old Trafford when Merv let fly with a high-powered

Toddy and Tubby — team-mates through and through. Pity only one of us is consistently making runs.

fire extinguisher in the direction of our pugnacious number three. The force of the blast pushed Boonie backwards into a potted palm but at no time did the nuggetty Taswegian spill a drop of his beer or let his cigarette go out — footwork and balance.

DAY 22 | JUNE 3

On the bus this morning there were more than a few seedy-looking faces. I think a few of us overdosed on the old tonsil varnish last night. There's no denying the Aussie team likes a drink, some would say a little too much. I remember having quite a lengthy discussion about this with Simmo once over a few beers in India. Basically, he thought we all drank too much. I recall pointing to four empty stubbies of VB in front of me and saying, 'Simmo, that's all I've had. Four stubbies mate, what's the big deal?' Before he got to answer we were called down to breakfast and the subject was never raised again.

The trip to Birmingham was livened up by a screening of *Basic Instinct* with Sharon Stone, on the bus video-system. Without a freeze-frame button the film lost some of its magic.

At 6.30 pm the whole squad gathered for the pre-Test naming of the 12 players (I'm in!!!), followed by quite a serious session in which Swampy asked us all to write an answer to the question, 'What is the one thing we must do in order to retain the Ashes?' You could answer anonymously, which thank God I did, because when Swampy started reading the guys' answers out they were things like 'Believe in ourselves' and 'Give 100 per cent as a team'. I'd written 'Drop Taylor'. Luckily Swampy skipped my answer.

The meeting was followed by another tour function, this time a dinner put on for us by Cornhill. As we were playing the day after tomorrow Tubs and Swampy invoked a strict midnight curfew; nothing but light beer to be drunk after 12.00.

DAY 23 | JUNE 4

Training the day before a Test is always intense.

Well, tomorrow's the big day. Our first Test. Training was more intense today, as you'd expect the day before a Test, with Tubs insisting we all play at least nine holes before lunch at the magnificent Belfry golf course.

There're still a few injury worries within the team: Bic's back is still troubling him, Bev will be playing with his groin, BJ's got a crook neck, and my liver's pretty stuffed. Not that you'll hear any one of us complaining. This, in my opinion, is one of the reasons Aussie teams have been so successful over the years; we're tough, we're committed and we're all united in the one goal — stopping some other bastard taking our place in the team. Winning would be good too.

As usual there were quite a few spectators and press hanging round, with most interest directed at Warney — not that he exactly shies away from it. His finger's not the only thing that gets a little swollen, if you know what I mean.* To be fair to the guy though, Warney is under enormous pressure and rarely out of the public eye. At his wedding to Simone in 1995 he was bombarded with offers from various women's magazines who were all after a photo scoop. To his credit Warney knocked 'em all back, only to have an unnamed guest sneak a camera in and sell the photos to a magazine for a five figure sum.

Warney and Simone's wedding. Photo: W. Todd, reprinted courtesy of *Australian Women's Day*

* I mean his head is too. Swollen that is. Like his finger, only metaphorically.

After training I had a few media commitments, including a live radio interview with Melbourne station 3AW. It's at moments like this I'm really thankful the ACB decided a few years back to provide every member of the Australian squad with lessons in dealing with the media. When you think about it, this policy makes good sense. Let's face it, not everyone has the natural ability to chat away fluently like an AB or Boonie. It takes practice. Personally, I believe I've really benefited from the program. Take this transcript of a radio interview I did in the late '80s before the media lessons:

```
INTERVIEWER:   Warwick Todd, thanks for joining us.
TODD:          No worries.
INTERVIEWER:   You've got a big game tomorrow.
TODD:          Sure have.
INTERVIEWER:   How do you think you'll go?
TODD:          Hopefully okay.
INTERVIEWER:   How's the knee holding up?
TODD:          Good.
```

Pretty embarrassing stuff, eh? Now here's how I'd handle the same questions today, with a bit more media savvy under my belt:

```
INTERVIEWER:   Warwick Todd, thanks for joining us.
TODD:          No worries mate.
INTERVIEWER:   You've got a big game tomorrow.
TODD:          Sure have mate.
INTERVIEWER:   How do you think you'll go?
TODD:          Hopefully okay mate.
INTERVIEWER:   How's the knee holding up?
TODD:          Oh mate! Good mate.
```

I don't know whether you noticed it but I dropped the word 'mate' in a little more often. It's a great way of appearing natural during an interview and avoiding the fact you've got no idea who you're talking to. All us Aussies use it. As an interesting footnote, the Poms took this strategy one step further in April of this year with their entire squad attending a course on public skills run by former England Rugby captain Will Carling. Carling, of course, used to be one of Princess Di's roots.*

At the pre-match team meeting tonight we discussed the best way to attack the Poms, with Tubs asking everyone for their thoughts. That's one of the great things about Tubby. Unlike skippers of old who only ever listened to the so-called 'senior' players, Tubs is interested in everyone's opinion. Warney's, Tugga's, Pigeon's, Lang's. Well, maybe not Lang's.

After Tubs spoke Swampy got up and said it was time for some tough decisions. In the end we decided to eat Italian before opting for an early night.

Unfortunately I didn't get much sleep as I was hot and the room was stuffy. Eventually at around 2.00 am I had to leave the nightclub and get a taxi back to the hotel.

*Had I attended the course I probably would have learnt not to say things like that.

DAY 24 JUNE 5

1st Cornhill Test Match, Edgbaston — Day 1

The team bus is always a quiet one on the first morning of a Test match. No one wants a lot of noise when you're hungover.

We won the toss and decided to bat, but disaster struck quickly with Tubs out for just 7. Watching him trudge back towards the dressing-room, we all felt for him. Almost wished we hadn't super-glued his kitbag to a bench, but there was no time for such sentimentality.

Unfortunately several other wickets followed as we struggled to consolidate on a difficult pitch tinged with green. Of course, it would be easy to detract from the fine performance of England's bowlers by placing too much emphasis on the *appallingly under-prepared* wicket we were forced to play on, and by going on about the fact it was well below international standards, and specifically tailored to suit the English swing attack, or even raising the possibility that Edgbaston

The Poms sure love their autographs. I've got no idea who the old guy is, but he still managed to pull a crowd.

should lose its Test match status (which it should). But let's not allow this to overshadow England's excellent effort.

An effort largely assisted by a deliberately substandard playing surface. I managed to compile a gritty 16 runs when, a few minutes before lunch, I got an edge to a Gough out-swinger and was caught behind. On being dismissed with so few balls remaining a rush of emotions go through your head: anger, disappointment, self-pity. In the end you've got to rise above all that and do the mature thing — blame the pitch. It really was a shocker.

We resumed after lunch (which was of excellent standard) but the rot had truly set in and we managed a total of just 118 runs. To make matters worse Dizzy tore a hammy and was forced to leave the field. I could tell he felt pretty bad so at the drinks break I had a quiet word, telling him not to feel he'd let the team down because he was bowling pretty poorly anyway.

By late afternoon the pitch seemed to have lost a lot of its movement and England finished the day at 3 for 200 with Hussain looking dangerous on 86 not out, a truly great effort.*

In these high-powered days of professional cricket, a tradition that seems to be dying is the two teams getting together at the end of a day's play and enjoying a drink. I'm pleased to say that at the end of today's play the English team was welcomed into our rooms. By a groundsman. We'd long since jumped on the bus and headed back to the hotel.

I was still feeling pretty angry about being dismissed so cheaply today and decided to give Ros a bell. It was great hearing her voice after so long and I chatted to her for ages before the tape on our answering machine ran out. I know a lot of the guys are really missing their better halves, but under tour rules the ladies aren't allowed to officially join us until six weeks into the tour. Of course, there's nothing stopping someone's wife or girlfriend coming across before that time, but it wouldn't really be much fun, following the team around day after day with nothing to do but sit and watch us play. Just ask Ricky Ponting.

* Given he was out lbw to Pigeon twice.

DAY 25 | JUNE 6 | 1st Cornhill Test Match, Edgbaston — Day 2

We woke this morning to a predictable lashing from the Pommy press. Headlines like 'Wilting Matilda' followed by articles suggesting Aussie team morale was at an all-time low. I admit it was a fairly sombre scene in our rooms last night, with very little beer drunk and only two verses of 'Khe Sahn' sung. I even noticed some of the guys not joining in the chorus. I guess the English papers don't often get to celebrate a home team success and you could tell they were getting pretty carried away with things by the front page of the normally conservative *Times*, featuring a topless woman with the headline 'Tit's All Over Aussies!'.

But I was annoyed by the continued emphasis on Tubby and his lack of form, with several journos basically suggesting that a team whose leader is struggling will often struggle itself. The fact is, we no longer think of Tubs as our leader — so what's the problem?

Coming out to field yesterday the entire team wore their baggy green caps. This was an idea of Tugga's last summer, as a way of presenting a unified team front. I remember the day he proposed it — we argued for hours. You see, a lot of the guys have sponsorship deals with different hat companies. In the end we agreed to all wear them for the first hour and after that — Tugga could get stuffed. It's a wonderful tradition that's continued to this day.

It was a good morning's play, marred only by a few heated exchanges in the field. Seems the Pommy batsmen didn't take kindly to the odd piece of 'friendly' advice offered to them at the crease. Personally, I think this shows great weakness from the England players. Over the years I've been called all sorts of things in the field: 'hopeless arsehole', 'spastic', 'miserable excuse for a cricketer'. That's just the nature of the Aussie slips cordon, we like to fire each other up.

Despite losing a few wickets England managed to extend their lead, ending the day 6 down and 231 runs in front. Off the field there was more bad news with Junior being rushed to hospital with severe stomach pains. They were so severe he was barely able to walk or maintain a conversation; I feel terrible that it took three days for any of us to notice.

After a big day in the field you want nothing more than a few quiet drinks but because of our so-called 'collapse' yesterday a lot of journos back in Australia were wanting interviews tonight. It's vital to keep a clear head for these. I'll never forget our World Cup semi-final win over the Windies in 1996. Celebrations in our dressing-room were in full swing, I was downing rums and Coke at a furious rate when someone grabbed me and asked if I'd do an interview for the press. I was pretty gone by this point but figured it was just some local paper, so I staggered outside. Imagine my surprise when there's an Australian camera crew waiting with a satellite link-up with Ray Martin on *A Current Affair*. I tell you, there's no quicker way of getting a bloke to sober up than by shoving a TV camera in his face. Just ask Mike Willessee. I may have been a little tired and emotional during that interview but from what those back home told me, I think I got away with it.

Transcript of *A Current Affair* interview conducted 14/3/96 between Ray Martin and Warwick Todd

MARTIN: Joining us live now from Mohali Stadium, Chandigarh in India, Australian batsman Warwick Todd. Mate, a great semi-final win?

TODD: We creamed 'em! Whipped their little black arses! Aussie, Aussie, Aussie, oy!

MARTIN: No doubt the team enjoyed the win?

TODD: Aussies mate. Aussie! Aussie! Aussie! Oy! (SINGS) The last train out of Sydney's almost gone…

MARTIN: Obviously having a few problems with the satellite there, we'll see if we can't catch up with the victorious Aussie team after the break.

TODD: We creamed the bastards! Whipped their little black…

(INTERVIEW TERMINATED)

DAY 26 | JUNE 7 | 1st Cornhill Test Match, Edgbaston — Day 3

England declared this morning at 9 for 478, but not before a few more heated verbal exchanges took place out on the field. Not surprisingly the English press got stuck into us for yesterday's on-field 'incidents', once again applying the 'ugly Australian' tag.

Okay, I'll be the first to admit that on-field behaviour has degenerated in recent years, and that yes, the Australian team has been involved in some unfortunate incidents. But I just wish the so-called experts in the press would look *behind* these incidents to the underlying reason why they're taking place. Take a few random examples from recent times:

- In '91 West Indies opener Desmond Haynes left his crease and actually threatened Ian Healy with his bat.

- A few years later there was a fiery exchange between West Indian hot-head Brian Lara and our 'keeper Ian Healy after video replays *allegedly* showed Heals had dropped the ball before stumping Lara.

- A few seasons after this during the Benson & Hedges series in 1996 our 'keeper Ian Healy was involved in an ugly war of words with Sri Lanka's captain Arjuna Ranatunga at the SCG.

- The following year during the Singer World Cup Heals was swept into a heated exchange with India's Azharuddin after *allegedly* being run out by him.

- Yesterday Devon Malcolm was involved in a nasty slanging match with Aussie 'keeper Ian Healy.

Now ask yourself, what's the one thing each of these have in common? Staring you in the face right? They're all incidents involving black players. Sure, I know it may not be 'politically correct' to say this, but in my opinion the decline in behavioural standards on cricket fields today is a direct result of the increased participation of non-Caucasion players. They simply lack the temperament for this gentlemen's game.

We started our second innings 360 runs behind the Poms. Naturally there was a fair bit of tension within the Aussie dressing-room and, being a superstitious lot, everyone remained in the exact positions they'd occupied during our first innings. Blewie and Kaspa near the door, Pigeon on the dunny, Junior doubled over in pain and me just outside the Ladbroke's tent.

To the relief of everybody Tubs finally broke the drought, scoring a magnificent 108 not out. By stumps we were only 104 runs behind with 9 wickets in hand. Naturally there were a few celebratory drinks after play and it was during these that Tubs received a fax from none other than the Prime Minister:

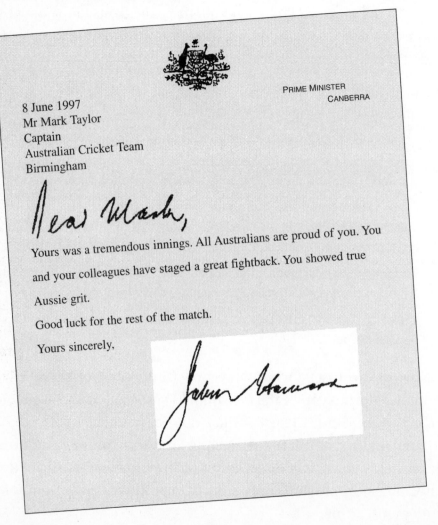

PRIME MINISTER
CANBERRA

8 June 1997
Mr Mark Taylor
Captain
Australian Cricket Team
Birmingham

Dear Mark,

Yours was a tremendous innings. All Australians are proud of you. You and your colleagues have staged a great fightback. You showed true Aussie grit.

Good luck for the rest of the match.

Yours sincerely,

John Howard

It brought back memories of a very special fax I once received from Canberra...

Undelivered notices should be returned to

Australian
Taxation
Office

ATO

PO Box 9990
Box Hill VIC 3128

**Your Tax File Number is
329 500 791 0XD**

MR WARWICK TODD
AUSTRALIAN CRICKET TEAM
ADELAIDE

Date of issue
6 SEP 93

Income Tax Assessment Act 1936
NOTICE OF PENALTY
For year ending 30 June 1993 (or substituted accounting period)

Notice is hereby given that if a tax return for the above period is not received by this office along with late payment penalty as previously detailed, court proceedings shall be immediately instituted.

Signed,

(Deputy Commissioner of Taxation)

P.S. Good luck for tomorrow's game !

DAY 27 JUNE 8

1st Cornhill Test Match, Edgbaston — Day 4

It was a good session for us this morning, with Tubs advancing to 129 before being caught and bowled Croft. Blewie also notched a century and by lunch we were 2 for 352, just 8 runs behind England. During lunch (again, of excellent standard) there was a real mood of optimism amongst the team, highlighted by the fact Herb found a sliver of broken glass in his mashed potato. The return of such good-natured team tomfoolery is a sure sign the boys are feeling better. Speaking of which, Junior was released from hospital this morning having been given the all-clear. According to the specialist he didn't have appendicitis and the chance of the stomach pains returning was 100 to 1. (Junior couldn't help himself and made a £10 bet).

One of the most common questions I'm asked by fans is, 'Do you players listen to the radio or TV commentary during a game?' Speaking personally, the answer's a big fat 'no'. However, during the afternoon session I just happened to overhear a bit of the BBC commentary, some old hack who probably played two county games was discussing our batting line-up and — get this — he starts questioning Michael Bevan's ability to handle the short stuff! Now I'm sorry, but Bevo has really worked on this aspect of his game and I just couldn't believe the crap I was hearing. I was so pissed off I just had to go out onto the balcony where Bevo was waiting and tell him what the guy had said. Not word for word, just a general summary to the effect that 'Michael Bevan proved yet again in the first innings his dreadful shortcomings against quality pace'. Come to think of it, it was word for word. Anyway, Bevo was speechless. Ten minutes later, Blewie's out, Bevo goes in, cops a short one from Gough and is out bunting the ball feebly into the gully. That's how damaging listening to radio commentaries can be.

Unfortunately our next five wickets also fell cheaply. I was out to an extremely dubious stumping decision, with the third umpire being called to consult his video replay. I don't know what video he was watching, it couldn't have been the one featuring my back foot firmly planted behind the crease, because the dreaded red light went on. We eventually ended our innings on 477, just 118 runs in front. It was never going to be an easy total to defend, especially when you consider the ongoing problems of our bowling line-up: Dizzy (hamstring), Warney (shoulder), Tugga (second rate bowler). Kaspa was our only bowler in good form but even he wasn't capable of preventing England knocking off the runs and going one up in the series.

Despite losing we were professional enough to join the England players for a few quiet drinks after the match. I was somewhat surprised to see former England skipper Graham Gooch make an appearance. Gooch and I had quite a few heated run-ins during the last Ashes series and the ill-feeling between us was still evident in the dressing-room tonight. That's one of the marvellous things about Test cricket; a hatred formed on the field is often something you'll have for the rest of your life.

When we arrived back at the hotel there was a message from Gabe Hirsh, my manager back home. I'd shot a magazine ad before I left and he was ringing to say the client was really pleased with it. Now I know a lot of people think cricketers shouldn't be making ads. And I agree — no one likes to see Dennis Lillee rolling around on a shagpile rug or AB pretending to enjoy Liptons tea. But we've all got to make a living, and put a little cash in the bank before we grow old, get dropped and end up doing crosses for Neville Oliver from the Bellerive Oval. However, I made it quite clear to my manager if I was going to do an ad it had to be for something classy — otherwise, no go. So you can imagine my delight when the folks at the Fine Pine Furniture Centre rang. Six grand for one photo shoot and that's it — we don't owe them another thing.

I think a lot of people have the wrong idea about Test cricketers and the money they make. If you think we all live in luxury houses, drive SAABs and fly first class from venue to venue, you'd be wrong.

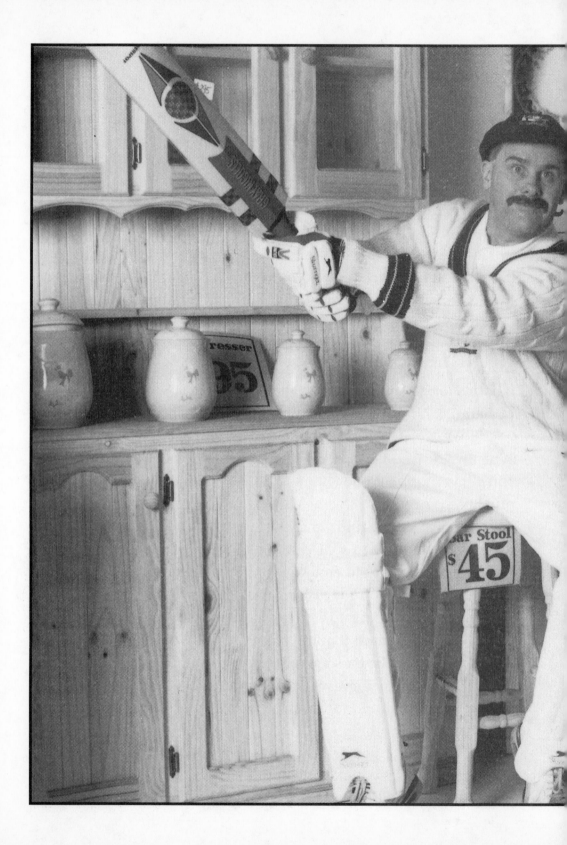

That sort of star treatment is reserved for rock stars, prime ministers and the odd blond leg-spin bowler. The rest of us do it a lot tougher. That's why I'm lucky to have Gabe. He's in charge of the Excel Sports Management Company. They're a new mob but they've already got quite an impressive array of talent on their books, including yours truly, and they know how to cut a deal. Gabe handles all my appearances, contract negotiations and publicity requests which, I can tell you, are pretty constant. Just a few days before leaving for this tour I was being chased by the Brisbane *Courier-Mail* for their celebrity 'Why I Wear What I Wear' column *and*, at the same time, getting calls from Grundy's wanting to use my face on the *Sale of the Century* fame-game board. Thank goodness I've got Gabe to sort all that stuff out.

My other main source of income (apart from match payments) comes from public speaking. It's something I've only got into recently, but it's a real buzz. Pays well too. Depending on the occasion Gabe can get me up to $4000 for a 20-minute talk, less his 51 per cent standard manager's cut. Of course, I don't always charge four grand; I did a talk a few weeks back and only asked for $500, but that was for friends. Interestingly, it was the first time I've done a eulogy. And possibly the last — I'm still waiting to be paid.

DAY 28 JUNE 9

**1st Cornhill Test Match,
Edgbaston — Day 5**

Considering yesterday's Test loss the mood in the Aussie camp this morning was surprisingly good, with most of the guys feeling positive about the future. That was until Swampy announced our planned golf day was off and instead we'd be heading back to the ground for an all-day training session.

As predicted, the local press continued their gloating today, with most articles going into great detail about our so-called 'weaknesses'. I felt particularly sorry for Pigeon who was singled out by the *Telegraph* for his 'consistent failure to maintain line and length'. As I said to the big fella, it was a nasty and unnecessarily vicious attack and journos shouldn't be able to write this sort of stuff, even if it is largely true.

Good news for the team with the announcement that Paul Reiffel will be joining us tomorrow to take over from the injured Dizzy. Pistol's a great competitor and, with a history of chronic back and hamstring strains, he rates as one of the fittest Aussie bowlers around.

After a big day of training we gathered at a Birmingham night-club for a few drinks and a bit of a party. Sure, we'd lost the Test but the venue had been booked weeks before and we didn't want to waste the deposit. Naturally no amount of alcohol can match the intoxicating feeling of winning a Test match (I know — I've done trials) but it still turned out to be a great night, as we partied on with various team officials and members of the Australian press contingent sharing in the fun. The party atmosphere continued during the bus trip back to our hotel with everyone dancing and drinking. It was great to see our driver enjoying himself so much. Finally back in Swampy's room, Day 5 of the first Test officially ended with one final rendition of 'Under the Southern Cross I Stand', led by Heals perched atop the mini-bar. Each member of the side embraced the guy next to him to form a tightly-knit circle. I don't think I've ever felt closer to a bunch of guys in my life.

DAY 29 JUNE 10

Michael Kasprowicz wants to kill me and McGrath's threatening to do the same. I swear, that's the last time I talk to any member of the press. All I said — and I don't even remember saying it — was, 'I thought our bowlers took it easy.'

Which is true! They could have gone harder. Blokes like Kaspa and Pigeon are capable of knocking over far tougher line-ups. I just meant they didn't really get an opportunity to. Trust a journo to twist your words. Anyway, Tubs and our manager Crommo said to lie low for a while and let them smooth it over. Nothing more was said between us for the rest of the day but when I got back to my room I discovered my bed had been short-sheeted, so I knew I was back in the good books. I guess you've always got to be a bit careful around fast bowlers, fiery customers that they are, but deep down they've all got hearts of gold. I'll never forget my first Test in Sydney, when Henry Lawson was our number-one strike bowler. He'd just delivered another thunderbolt past some quivering batsman's head and was walking back to his mark when I nervously underarmed the ball back to him. It missed by 6 inches and rolled past him towards the boundary. Naturally I copped a fair razzing from the crowd as I ran to retrieve it, and when I handed it back all he could say was, 'Learn to throw, a*#ehole'. I knew then I was part of the team.

Another official function tonight saw the post-match celebrations continue in earnest.

DAY 30 | JUNE 11

**Australia vs.
Nottinghamshire — Day 1**

Not a great start to the day. At breakfast I was dragged aside by Swampy and Crommo and reprimanded over a pretty trivial incident the night before. We were out last night having a few drinks at an official function when Slats, Junior and I got a bit carried away. I'll admit it — a table was knocked over and a few vases were broken. But talk about being hauled over the coals! We were just letting off a bit of steam. So what if we're never invited back to Buckingham Palace?

To make matters worse, I seem to have picked up a nasty dose of flu. My body's so stiff and aching it feels like I spent the night sleeping in a gutter (whereas I know for a fact I couldn't have been there more than two hours before the cops woke me). A trip to the

Despite play being called off I was still happy to entertain the small crowd with a few balcony antics. Here I'm in the middle of my famous 'pissed Queen Mother' impersonation which later attracted a fair bit of criticism in the press. How was I to know they had microphones there?

local doctor confirmed the news — flu — and I was prescribed a course of antibiotics. The doctor warned me these were not to be taken with alcohol, so for the next few days I'll have to do the sensible thing and not take them.

Fortunately I'm being rested from this match so that guys like Ponts and Slats can get a go. Also in the team is Paul Reiffel, who arrived here last night. Pistol's a top bloke who should really boost our depleted bowling line-up. Tugga is acting captain, taking over from Tubs who has been acting as a captain for the last six months.

As it turned out there was no play today due to rain, which was a real nuisance. Not only are we all in need of valuable match practice, there's an excellent beer garden here at Trent Bridge we were simply unable to use all day.

In order to fill in the day we decided to hold our first fines meeting for the tour. These meetings are a lot of fun and a great way of bringing the boys together. Fines are generally imposed for trivial things like snoring, sleeping in and missing the bus, choosing dud restaurants for team meals. I kicked proceedings off by light-heartedly fining Bich for developing a back injury and letting the team down, effectively causing us to lose the first Test and arguably the entire one-day series. For some reason he took this personally and things turned nasty. Honestly, some blokes wouldn't recognise a good-natured joke if it bit 'em on the balls.

DAY 31 JUNE 12

**Australia vs.
Nottinghamshire — Day 2**

Sad news today with confirmation that Andy Bichel will be sent home, after tests revealed a stress-related problem in his back. To really add insult to injury, Bich's wife arrived in England this morning to be with her husband. We held a quick team meeting and agreed there was only one decent course of action — let Bich go home but his wife can stay.

Even though I'm not playing in this match against Notts, all members of the team are expected to attend games for the first six weeks of the tour. Only after that are you allowed to drink on your own. There's always plenty to do in the rooms, even if you're not playing. This morning I set about adding my signature to several dozen bats we'll be donating for charity auctions. I then added Tub's, Bevo's and Junior's signatures before passing the bats on for someone else to forge the rest. We donate a lot of signed tour merchandise to charities and I'm always happy to be involved. Although, on a personal note, I think charities can be a bit of a two-edged sword. Take this mob I was involved with a few years back. I won't name them here, but they ran activities for children with cancer.* Basically, all I had to do was roll up at the odd celebrity golf day, get photographed standing between Sam Newman and some bald kid, and people thought you were a saint. Not that I was doing it because of what people thought; my motives were a little higher than that. I enjoy golf. Besides, I think anyone in the public eye has a duty to give of themselves, and to be seen doing it. Sets a good example.

Anyway, they had this charity golf day in '94, I give of myself, play all day, sign autographs etc. Go along to the dinner, there's a raffle — I do the right thing and buy a few tickets. Next thing they ask me to draw the winning ticket and would you believe it, it's me! You could have heard a pin drop in the room. Naturally I'm stoked — first prize

* Challenge Cancer Support Network.

is a Toyota Celica. I'm just about to phone Ros with the good news when the bloke in charge sidles up and whispers in my ear that perhaps I should 'donate' the prize back. Doesn't think it'll 'look good if someone involved with the organisation wins first prize in its raffle'. 'That's easily fixed,' I said. 'I'll end my involvement.' Which I did, driving off at the wheel of the Celica. There's no doubt charity work has its rewards.

Tugga won the toss and sent Notts into bat. By mid-afternoon we had them all out for 239. Most promising was the form of Pistol who was immediately back to his old self, taking a wicket in his second over and calling for a back brace a few balls later. We ended the day at 1 for 51 with Herb looking dangerous and Ponts just hanging on.

DAY 32 JUNE 13

**Australia vs.
Nottinghamshire — Day 3**

Centuries to both Herb and Tugga today saw Australia cruise to 5 for 398 before rain finally caused the match to be called off. The last few days of sitting around doing nothing and eating stodgy food has seen me pile a few kilos on, and so after a few mandatory drinks with the Notts boys I decided it was time to start doing something serious about it. It was a tough few hours, but I eventually managed to find a tailor who could let my pants out.

Back at the hotel I was just about to jump in the shower when the phone rang. It was my sister, and she sounded upset. Turned out our family dog's had to be put down after biting a kid. I couldn't believe it! Rocky and I grew up together and I've never known him to bite anyone without me ordering him to. It's very unusual behaviour for a kelpie cross. Then again, he was a kelpie crossed with a pit bull.

Another official function tonight, this one livened up by the presence of some rather enthusiastic female cricket fans. So enthusiastic that let's just say a few of the unmarried team members had a little 'company' back at the hotel, if you know what I mean.*

Being a committed family man I naturally behaved myself. Mind you, things used to be a little different in my younger days. Back in the mid-1980s I captained a junior Australian team to England. I was

Rocky — he'd never bite anyone without being ordered to.

* The girls came back and they had sex.

rooming with another player who never made it at first-class level so I can probably mention his name — Mark Newman. Anyway, those of us with girlfriends back home tended to play things pretty straight and just drink but the other 'bachelors', including Newmo, would put the hard word on just about anything in a skirt. One night I came back to my room, walked in and there's Mark on the divan with some local waitress. I take one look and say, 'What do ya think you're doing?' He replies, 'Come on Toddy — I'm unattached.' I say, 'Not from this angle you don't seem to be!' (That one always goes down a treat at sportsmen's nights.)

Of course, sharing rooms can make nocturnal activities a little problematic for those involved. Little wonder our team physio Errol 'Hooter' Alcott is so popular — he's one of the lucky few with a room of his own. It's said that for a dozen cold ones Hooter will let you (and your 'companion') use his room for half an hour. For two dozen he'll even wait outside.

DAY 33 JUNE 14

**Australia vs.
Leicestershire — Day 1**

At last I seem to have thrown off this cold but there were quite a few new non-starters at breakfast this morning, victims of the infamous traveller's tummy. I tell you, you've got to be so careful what you eat overseas, regardless of whether it's India or England. Even the most cautious eater can expect a few bouts of gastro per tour. Last night Gilly was suffering quite badly and I can tell you from experience, when you've gotta go you've gotta go! An unpleasant predicament for our reserve 'keeper, made no better by Warney and Tugga sneaking into his room while he was out and covering the dunny seat with Gladwrap.

Arriving at the ground it was disappointing to discover yet again that the visiting team's dressing-room was about quarter the size of the home team's. This, combined with a substandard lunch consisting of mashed potato and cabbage, made for a very trying day.

Another difficult factor was the weather, with frequent showers sweeping across the ground. Rain interruptions can play havoc with your concentration and the ability to cope with them is vital for an Ashes tour member. Inevitably, just as play gets started and you've settled into a rhythm the weather will change and you'll be forced to down cards and get out on the field. Not easy when you're sitting on a full house.

As it turned out, play was delayed for about two hours. Eventually the skies cleared, Leicestershire won the toss and we were sent in to bat. Tubs was out for 1, to an absolute 'jaffa'.* He was followed by a few other quick wickets, with Ponts being the only one to reach 50. I was dismissed for 37, the victim of a very poor umpiring decision. I received a real lifter from Mullally and was given out caught behind off the glove. I immediately indicated to the umpire that the ball had

---

* A 'jaffa' is a ball that a batsman is pretty much incapable of playing. In Tubs' case this covers most deliveries he's faced so far on tour.

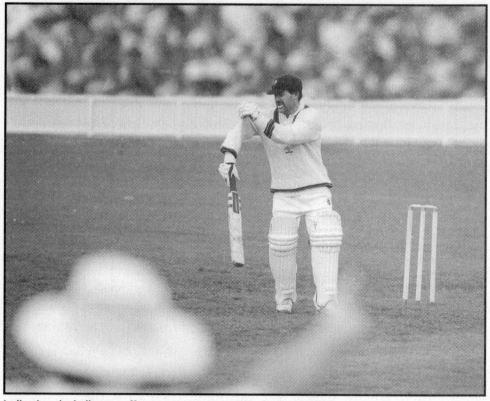

Indicating the ball came off my arm. Not easy with a broken hand.

in fact come off my upper arm by grabbing the sleeve, but this was ignored. I think it's a sad state of affairs when an umpire chooses to uphold an appeal rather than listen to a batsman who's made the effort to guide him to a fair decision. And it was an effort, grabbing my sleeve, as my hand felt like it had just been broken.

DAY 34 | JUNE 15

Australia vs. Leicestershire — Day 2

Play was delayed another 90 minutes this morning due to rain. When we finally got to start Tubs decided he would declare at our overnight score of 8 for 220. Leicestershire's openers came out and Pistol was immediately in the action, picking up the wicket of Maddy in his second over. Pigeon also bowled well, forcing Macmillan to pop a catch up to short backward square leg. It was a sharp chance, but nothing too difficult for a decent fielder. Unfortunately BJ was there and the ball went to ground.

Our only bowler to really struggle was Warney who copped a fair bit of curry, not only from the Leicestershire batsmen, but also from a group of spectators sitting on the roof of an adjoining pub. These idiots, obviously full of ink, jeered and heckled our number-one leg-spinner every time he conceded a boundary. It was a relief when they were finally ordered back to the Channel 9 commentary box.

In an effort to manufacture a result the home team declared at 4 for 62, before rain forced us from the ground yet again. Off field the question mark over Warney's poor form continued with one journo alleging our 'Earl of Twirl' needed a shoulder operation. Hooter responded with 'Rubbish, absolute rubbish.' I then quipped good-naturedly, 'Much like what he was bowling today!'

It was a long walk home from the ground. Back at the hotel I decided to put a call through to my father, as tomorrow is his birthday. Dad will be 83, but he's still as sharp as a tack. Ask him who was Australia's wicket-keeper from 1965 to 1969 and quick as a flash he'll answer you 'Wally Grout'. Then again, ask him if he wants a cup of tea and he'll say the same thing. Some sort of fixation, according to the geriatric specialist at Mont Calm. Dad was my first coach, and he was very strict. Some of his methods bordered on the illegal. Not that he ever pushed any of us Todd kids into cricket. We were always given the choice, between playing or getting beaten with a length of

Dad never played first-class cricket but his father was a member of the 1921 Ashes squad. That's Pops, seated third from the left.

electrical cord. After Mum was killed (or, I should say 'died' — the coroner returned an open finding), Dad moved in with Ros and me. Putting him into a home a few years later was one of the hardest decisions we ever had to make, but with two kids and nowhere else to store my trophies we simply had to free up the spare room. It was either Dad or the billiard table.

DAY 35 | JUNE 6

**Australia vs.
Leicestershire — Day 3**

I tell you what, if the Pommy press aren't bagging you they're going overboard with praise. There was an article in the *Mirror* this morning rating every player on the current Ashes tour. According to their experts, W. Todd is 'amongst the finest batsmen of the last decade'. To be perfectly honest I was rather embarrassed by this, and said so to a few of the guys on the bus coming in. They claimed they hadn't seen the article, which is crap, because I'd made photocopies for the whole team.

Warwick Todd — amongst the finest batsmen of the last decade.

For once play started on time this morning, with Tubs compiling a vintage half-century. He was eventually out for 57. A few more quick wickets saw yours truly at the crease, right in the middle of an inspired spell from local bowler James Ormond. I'm telling you, this guy was moving the ball like nobody's business! During the course of the morning I was struck three sickening blows to the groin. Two from Ormond and one from Tubs when I walked back into the dressing-room after getting out attempting to hook.

We eventually declared at 105, leaving the home side a target of 264. Thanks to fine performances from all our bowlers (and seven overs of rubbish from Bevan) Leicestershire were all out for 179, giving us our first real victory in weeks. Imagine our surprise then when Swampy interrupted the post-match celebrations and started criticising our performance! According to our coach, too many of us were still concentrating on personal goals rather than focusing on the team as a whole. He then announced there'd be an all-day practice session tomorrow, which really pissed me off as I'd just organised to have lunch with a new equipment sponsor.

DAY 36 JUNE 17

Despite our impressive win yesterday the local press are still questioning our ability to win the second Test this week. One of the most outrageous accusations I read this morning was that we 'lacked courage'. Unbelievable! That is something I have never known an Australian player to lack. In 1991 David Boon was hit full in the face by Patrick Patterson and stitched up without an anaesthetic. He then insisted on going back out and continuing his innings. Would you say Boonie lacked courage? Brains maybe, but never courage. Same goes for the team today.

The coach to Lord's left at 9.00 am sharp for our all-day practice session. Or so they told me at reception when I wandered down for breakfast around 11.00. Needless to say, a cab was hailed and I soon arrived at the home of cricket. The fabled arena, the hallowed turf. Just being at Lord's gives you a thrill. There's something about the place. No wonder Catholics still flock there in search of miracles.

Needless to say, today's net session was pretty full-on and by the time we got back to the hotel we were all just about knackered. So imagine how we felt when Swampy announced tomorrow would be more of the same. Not surprisingly, several of us more senior players decided it was time to get together for a quiet 'chat' and so, after a few drinks that evening, we headed back to my room to discuss ways of dealing with the situation. As the informal meeting went on and a few more drinks were poured, we eventually agreed that it was time we demanded Swampy's resignation. Naturally we all appreciated the sensitive nature of the meeting and vowed to stay quiet about it for the time being. So imagine my surprise when five minutes later Swampy storms up to me, mad as a cut snake. Turns out he knows all the details we discussed, word for word. It was as if he was in the bloody room. Turned out he was. We've gotta stop holding sensitive meetings when we're pissed.

DAY 37 JUNE 18

Fortunately, today's practice session was cut short by rain and we were given the afternoon off. Three weeks into the tour and I decided I couldn't put it off any longer — it was washing day. It actually felt good soaking in a bath and I didn't really want to get out, but we had an official function to attend — only about the four hundreth of the tour so far. What makes these events even more tiresome is that just about everyone in England seems to own an autograph book and automatically expects you to fill it in. Well today I finally put the foot down and said, 'No, no more autographs.' Sure, I was sad to disappoint those kids, but they're bound to have plenty of other celebrities visiting the Burns Unit.

The routine before a Test match remained the same, with team manager Allan Crompton scheduled to say a few words (5.00 to 6.30) followed by Tubs and Swampy. Both our captain and our coach stressed the need to stay focused for the full five days, not to let ourselves

More celebrity starved English autograph hunters. I mean, you know when Gilly draws a crowd things must be a little desperate.

down by a lapse in concentration halfway through. They spoke about quite a few other things too, but to tell the truth I sort of drifted off.

After the traditional team meal I hit the sack early, planning to focus on tomorrow's match. Cricket is such a mental game and for the past few years I've drawn a lot of guidance from a book by renowned American sports psychologist Howard Friedell. The book is called *Thinking to Win*, and to my horror I realised this evening I hadn't thought to pack it. No point looking for another copy over here, it was such a best-seller that I'm told it's now out of print. Thankfully I can remember a lot of Howard's five-point 'thinking to win' plan, as it's been part of my game strategy for quite a while. What you have to do is:

1) Set a goal.
2) Visualise the goal.
3) Actualise the goal.
4) (something about positive thinking)
5) And point 5 escapes me.

DAY 38 JUNE 19

**2nd Cornhill Test,
Lord's — Day 1**

Early start, down to breakfast at 8.00. I tucked into a big plate of fried bacon and eggs along with several servings of french toast followed by two ginseng tablets which are supposed to be good for cholesterol. I'm very careful about my diet. As a touring cricketer I know how easy it is to let yourself slip. We've all seen Boonie in the shower. Back home I only eat foods with the word 'lite' misspelt after them. I actually have a personal nutritionist, Bernice ('Bernie') Quail, who writes out a long list of foods I should avoid. I pin this list to the door of the fridge and avoid it.

Bernie takes her job quite seriously and really throws herself into it. Not that she's got that much else to do. Her husband walked out on her two years back.*

Mind you, I always take care to avoid those fad diets that pop up in sports circles from time to time. Probably the worst of these occurred in India back in 1996 when several of our middle order began each day by drinking urine. Each others.

Down at the ground it was a pretty soggy old scene. Pools of water lying about, people huddling for shelter under umbrellas, everything soaked. How Glenn McGrath managed to get hold of that fire hose in our dressing-room is anyone's bet, but at least it helped take our minds off the fact there'd be no play.

Much is being made in the local press about the fact England have an unchanged line-up for this Test. All the journos are raving about the Poms' new-found 'unity' and praising the man behind it, Lord MacLaurin. According to one scribe MacLaurin is some sort of genius because he wrote to every English player after the one-day series, congratulating them and sending a bottle of champagne. Sorry to tell you fellas, but this practice has been part of the Aussie game plan for

---

* I don't know why I mentioned that, it's private and not really relevant.

years. Just a few weeks back when Tubs scored his century at Edgbaston, Swampy immediately arranged to send him a slab of beer. And he would have done so, except it wouldn't fit in the drinks trolley.

With play officially called off after lunch we returned to the hotel where I received some disturbing news from Gabe regarding my Limited Edition Warwick Todd Souvenir Testimonial Bat. We released this little earner last summer and sales have been quite good so far but apparently it may now have to be recalled after allegations from the Australian Conservation Foundation surfaced back home this week that the Limited Edition Oak Case the bat comes in may actually be made from rainforest timber. For God's sake, things like this really give me the pip. How a bunch of greenie troublemakers with long hair and bushy beards (and I'm not just talking about the blokes here) can knock an honest Aussie sportsman who's just trying to make an honest quid is a bloody disgrace. If you ask me, that's what's wrong with Australia today; it's full of bureaucratic do-gooders intent on sticking their noses into everyone else's business. That's why we decided to have the bat cases manufactured in Manila in the first place. That, and the fact it was so dirt cheap.

DAY 39 JUNE 20

2nd Cornhill Test, Lord's — Day 2

I guess it's every Australian cricketer's dream to represent his country in a match at Lord's. This fabled arena, steeped in tradition, represents the pinnacle of Test cricket. Which makes it even more surprising I managed to sleep through the alarm this morning and almost missed the team bus.

The local press were up to their old tricks, suggesting the Aussie team was 'hopelessly divided' and that morale was 'at an all-time low'. Honestly, where do they get this sort of crap from? Probably leaked by BJ or Ponts, both still pretty pissed off about not making the team. Speaking personally, I really don't mind what the press write but I do get angry when it's based on pure hearsay. Mark Ray of the *Sunday Age* is often guilty of doing that, or so I'm told.

Fortunately the rain cleared overnight and play was able to start on time. In his pre-match address Tubs said he believed we are playing well and that we just have to learn to back ourselves. Bit late I'm afraid — I'd already put £75 on the Poms to win. Tubs won the toss and elected to send the Poms in, though not without some hesitation. All morning he'd been agonising over the matter, saying we'd bat and then changing his mind. Watching Tubs struggle I couldn't help thinking about his predecessor AB, who never had a moment's hesitation over such decisions. He was a decisive leader and, in some ways, I think we still miss him. I know I do. He was a great player, a great captain and a great bloke. After his testimonial game in Brisbane in December 1994, all of us who played received a leather-bound copy of his autobiography *Beyond Ten Thousand*. When I got home I found he'd written inside the cover page 'To the best batsman I've ever played with, best wishes, Allan Border'. Turned out I'd taken Steve Waugh's copy by mistake.

As it turned out, Tubs made the right decision to send England in, and by the time rain stopped play they were 3 down for just 38. Star of the session was Pigeon, who took all three wickets and could well have had a fourth when Thorpe edged one to Heals. It looked out to me but apparently Heals had some doubts and went over to the umpires to ask the obvious question, 'Do you think the cameras picked that one up?' The answer was 'yes' and our 'keeper was forced to withdraw the appeal.

When rain finally halted play we headed back to the hotel and spent the afternoon winding down with a few quiet drinks. It's not always easy to relax after a big day (or morning) in the field. You have a few beers but the adrenalin keeps pumping. You have another beer and chat some more. Next thing you know, it's midnight. Another few beers. It's dawn. Another beer. You're taking the field on Day 3.

DAY 40 | JUNE 21

**2nd Cornhill Test,
Lord's — Day 3**

Thanks to an inspired bowling performance this morning from Pigeon the Poms crashed to be all out for 77, with the big New South Welshman snaring 8 for 38. It was a magnificent spell, especially given his first Test figures of 2 for 149. Asked by one journo about this amazing turnaround in form Pigeon was quoted as saying, '[I] had a pretty good day, you know [it was] good, [I] found my rhythm [and)] stuff, I hit [the] crease hard[er] than before and, [you] know, it was [good]'. I remember now why Tubs doesn't like him doing interviews.

With England all out it was our turn to pad up. Before commencing an innings is the time you find a lot of superstitions creeping into the game. Tugga will never go out to bat without his lucky red rag. Warney has a pair of lucky creams he once took 8 for 71 in. Our openers are interesting too. Elliot will never go out until he's walked anti-clockwise round the dressing-room, while Tubs insists on always scratching his left nut. His own left nut, not Elliot's.

Tubs and Herb both went out to face the English quicks without helmets, a move guaranteed to induce some 'chin music'. Most spectators watching on no doubt thought they were pretty brave doing this but the truth was we'd hidden their helmets, thigh guards and protectors on the team bus and they had no choice.

Good-natured prankery aside, there was a fair bit of tension in the Aussie dressing-rooms. We really needed a big team innings to stamp our authority on the match. For someone who hasn't been there it's hard to describe the hothouse atmosphere of the Aussie dressing-room. You've got cricket gear and bags strewn all over the floor, clothes hanging from every available hook, fans waiting outside one door, journos outside another, emotions overheated by the claustrophobic atmosphere and everyone focused on the one thing — finding memorabilia. The fact is we've all got testimonials coming up and there's only so much to go round.

Sorry fellas, this stump's mine. There's only so much memorabilia to go around.

A few quick wickets (including Tubs for 1) saw yours truly come to the crease at a fairly precarious time.

The actual route from dressing-room to the playing area at Lord's is quite a complex one. You have to follow various sets of stairs, head through the members' dining room and then find the correct door leading to the playing arena. Not easy when you're a nervous newcomer. I well remember my first match at Lord's many years ago when I got completely lost en route to the field, eventually opening a door and stumbling into the ladies loo! I don't know who was more surprised, me or Phil Tufnell.*

By the time I took guard the ball was moving both ways off the pitch and it was a struggle to just keep my wicket intact. But eventually the runs started to flow — it was simply a question of picking the gaps or hitting towards Devon Malcolm.

My stay at the crease was marred by only one unfortunate incident involving — surprise, surprise — the local press, who seem hell-bent

---

* Not a completely true story but one that always goes down a treat at sportsmen's nights.

on whipping up controversy wherever they can. What happened was I needed a new pair of batting gloves and signalled this fact in the standard way by holding up my middle finger to the Lord's Members' Pavilion. Next thing I'm being accused of making offensive gestures!

But this incident aside, it was a good day at the crease for yours truly and when play ended I was 43 not out, all set for a big score tomorrow.

Naturally there was some pretty serious celebrating after the day's play, with Pigeon's bowling performance being roundly toasted by the boys. Swampy even grabbed a felt pen and added 'G. McGrath 8/38' to the Lord's honours board. I then grabbed the pen and added breasts and a moustache to a portrait of the Queen. Some short guy in a suit started telling me off but I was so far gone by this point I just poured a can of VB over his head and walked away.

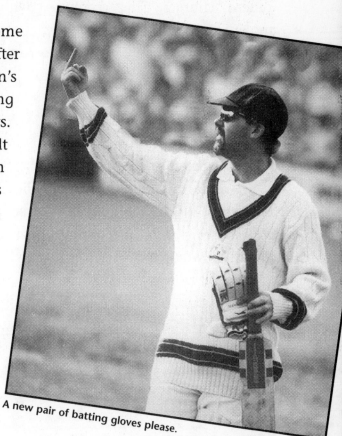

A new pair of batting gloves please.

DAY 41 JUNE 22

**2nd Cornhill Test,
Lord's — Day 4**

Crommo informed me this morning that I have to write a personal letter of apology to the Australian Prime Minister or I could face Federal charges. This, combined with a massive hangover, didn't make for a great start to the day.

Unfortunately things were looking even gloomier down at the ground with rain threatening to halt play indefinitely. When we finally got to resume our innings Tubs said he wanted quick runs and so Blewie and I really put the foot down. With a bit of luck and some sweetly timed stroke-making I was able to comply and, shortly after lunch, reached my first Test century at Lord's.

It was a marvellous moment, holding the bat aloft as the guys assembled on the balcony. Of course, cricket's a great leveller and I was out two overs later playing forward to a quicker delivery from Gough. It was a stupid stroke to play and I could have kicked myself

Well, they were already broken anyway.

but you've gotta accept these things, so instead I kicked the stumps. Well they were already broken anyway. When rain eventually halted play we were well placed at 7 for 213.

Day 4 at Lord's is traditionally when the Queen visits. Sure enough, the Protocol Man from Buckingham Palace had come to our dressing-rooms at the luncheon interval to tell us what to do when we were introduced — bow slightly and preface all comments with 'Your Majesty'. This came quite naturally to most of us older players as it was precisely how Simmo used to like to be addressed. Despite the coaching I was still pretty nervous when both teams lined up in our blazers during the tea interval, not to mention quite proud. Seeing Tubs escorting Queen Elizabeth II down the line I felt the moisture well up, and cursed those two quick beers I'd sunk. But there was no time to dash off and I soon found myself being introduced to the Queen. We ended up having quite a chat. Of course, it would be a serious breech of royal protocol to reveal what was discussed. Needless to say, if Fergie thinks she's going to be allowed to convert those stables at Sandringham into a private residence, she's got another think coming.

Celebrations kicked on back at the hotel for quite a few hours. Thanks largely to my century Australia is now 36 runs in front and there's a real feeling that we can win it from here, if the rain just holds off. Lying in bed that night I could hear the congratulatory faxes from home being passed under the door. My new roomie Tugga had failed with the bat so, out of consideration to him, I refrained from jumping up and reading the dozens of messages as they came in. That treat could wait for the morning.

A once-in-a-lifetime thrill. The Queen gets to meet Warwick Todd.

DAY 42 JUNE 23

2nd Cornhill Test, Lord's — Day 5

Sure enough there were at least 20 pages under my door this morning. Turned out it was an itemised account for the mini-bar.

Tubs decided to declare at our overnight score of 213, giving us a real chance of victory if we could just bowl the Poms out. Unfortunately things didn't start well with our skipper dropping a regulation snick from Butcher in Pistol's third over. Pigeon and Kaspa also struggled, bowling a little too full. The only Aussie bowler showing any promise was Warney; he not only snared two wickets but his grunting was at last back to full volume. Eventually the match was called off in the final hour with England 4 for 266.

Despite the match ending in a draw it was obvious Australia had scored a psychological victory, and celebrations within the Aussie dressing-room soon got under way in earnest. Although I'd be lying to say there weren't a few raised eyebrows over the choice of Man of the Match — Glenn McGrath. Sure, his record-breaking haul of 8 for 38 in the first innings was a great effort, but let's face it — he fell apart in the second. His first two deliveries this morning were wide down the leg side. And final figures of 1 for 65 when he should have been spearheading an Aussie onslaught are nothing if not a little pathetic. Compare this to my first innings century. Without wanting to go into details (114 runs, 171 balls, 17 boundaries and a superb six over long on) it was a pretty accomplished knock. Add to that my part in the dismissal of Hussain (caught and bowled Warney two balls after I came up with the nickname 'Saddam' and began using it from silly point), and you'd think the decision would be cut and dried. However, to question the process by which Man of the Match awards are handed out would be to detract from Pigeon's fine performance and I have no intention of doing that on this page.

After most games we like to enjoy a few quiet drinks in the rooms.

Dizzy and Pigeon in the Aussie rooms after a game. Dizzy was later fined under ACB Standing Order 23 for not 'having a prescribed alcoholic beverage in his hand during post-match proceedings'.

When faced with an lbw appeal never look guilty. Instead, there's a range of subtle expressions I like to employ. Start with a casual 'What?'

Follow this up with 'You're f#*king kidding!'

If desperate, try 'The ball was two feet outside off-stump you blind twerp!' If the umpire's finger remains up then there's only one thing to do...

...exit the arena with as much dignity as you can manage.

As worn by Warwick Todd!

GO-GLARE

Go-Glare
GLASSES

Stylish! Unbreakable! Reduces up to 23% of harmful UV rays!

I'd be lying to say there weren't a few raised eye-brows over the choice of Man of the Match.

The award is a joke. Time and time again flamboyant, brainless fast bowlers are rewarded rather than gifted, skilful batsmen. You should have seen McGrath strutting round at the pub like King Dick. Still, good luck to him; it's great to see someone not overly endowed with natural talent making use of what little they've got.

DAY 43 JUNE 24

Reading this diary you've probably noticed by now that I'm not someone who feels comfortable writing about his own achievements. Frankly, I wouldn't even know my tour average. Although it would have to be pretty good. Somewhere in the region of 38 or 39. Probably closer to 39. Certainly up there with the best, especially considering I haven't played every match and allowing for the rain interruptions and the times I've thrown my wicket away in the interests of the team, which is something I'm always prepared to do unlike certain other members of the squad who shall remain nameless.* The point is, I'm not in this game for personal glory; truth be told, I'm an intensely shy person. When I'm not starring with the bat for Australia I like nothing more than slipping out of the limelight. Not that it's always possible. Take this morning, for example. As the bus wasn't

* Michael Bevan.

I'd give anything to be an anonymous face in the crowd.

leaving until lunchtime I decided to wander round London and pick up a few presents for the family. In the space of two hours I must have been stopped a dozen times by fans desperate for an autograph. It's moments like these I'd give anything to just be an anonymous face in the crowd.

Our bus left London at 2.00 pm and en route we were pleased to spot the famous Golden Arches. Quick stop saw me down two quarter pounders and a large fries. I felt a little guilty about breaching my diet so I made sure I washed it all down with a Diet Coke.

A short while later we arrived at the Oxford Moathouse and checked in. I overheard a couple of the blokes arranging to go for a drink before dinner. I've been noticing over the past weeks a few cliques developing within the squad. As a senior player I know how divisive this can be — we really must function as a unified group — so I decided to take a few of the lads aside and have a word with them. Kaspa, Punter, Lang. We thought of asking Dizzy and BJ but none of us really likes them.

DAY 44 | JUNE 25

**Australia vs. British
Universities — Day 1**

Woke this morning to yet another wet day. This rain seems to be
cursing us. It seems ages since we've had a day's play that hasn't
been interrupted by the weather. Not that we're letting the situation
get us down. With play officially called off today I took the opportunity to visit Oxford's gymnasium. It's an excellent facility with first
class weight-training gear, rowing machines, treadmills, bikes and
circuit equipment, all of which you can see from the sauna, which is
where I spent the entire morning.

After lunch back at the hotel we sat around and watched a few
videos before Hooter announced a team training run. We were divided
into two groups, one led by Tubs, the other by Tugga, and set off. I was
with Tugga's group and we completed the 4 kilometre course in just
under three hours; not a bad effort when you consider the number of
pubs we had to visit.

Swampy takes fitness training very seriously — and you know it's going to be a serious session when
he puts the track suit on. That's my arse, back right, partially obscured by Pigeon's arse.

This evening we had yet another official function, a buffet dinner put on by the Parks Cricket Club. Turned out to be a pretty ritzy affair, with fine wine and food on offer, plus a surprise appearance by a group of Aussie supporters who gatecrashed the invitation-only affair by posing as journos. Once inside they began tucking into the seafood platter with gusto. Can't really blame them, these cricket devotees, most of whom have given up their jobs to slum round England in hostels to support their heroes. They're a good bunch of blokes and I felt bad about dobbing them in to security, but there were only so many prawns to go round. It was during this function that Blewie surprised us all by announcing he'd just got himself engaged. Naturally there were a few celebratory ales drunk to commemorate the event, with all the guys keen for details. Turns out the future Mrs Blewett is a 21-year-old Gold Coast girl called Jodie Williams. According to Blewie, his fiancee likes cricket but isn't all that passionate or knowledgeable about it. They should make a great pair.

Interestingly, this is the third 'Ashes Wedding' I've heard about. On the last tour in '93 Warney proposed to Simone during a boat trip up the Thames. And before that in '89 I popped the question to Ros. I remember the occasion very clearly, it was quite romantic, I even got down on one knee. She was bowling to me in the nets and I'd just played a sweep shot when I yelled out, 'You wanna get married?' And that marriage is now history.

DAY 45 JUNE 26

**Australia vs. British
Universities — Day 2**

More wet weather this morning ruled out any chance of play. Rather than sit around watching telly in our rooms all day, Hooter organised for a video and TV to be set up in the hotel dining room. A lot of the guys are getting pretty frustrated about missing out on so many matches but the fact is boredom is just part and parcel of an Ashes tour. There's always going to be rain, there's always going to be delays, there's always going to be speeches from Crommo. You've just got to accept it.

After lunch my roomie Lang and I returned to our room for a few housekeeping chores. He had some letters to write and I had quite a bit of gear that needed attention — boots to be whitened, pads dried etc. I noticed one of my batting shoes was missing a few spikes; this seemingly minor problem can actually be quite serious

Two of the legends of the game signing autographs. Well, Lillee would sign — Thommo would just sort of make a cross.

because without spikes you can easily slip and twist an ankle. Fortunately it was easily fixed, by swapping my shoes for a pair of Lang's when he wasn't looking.

Later this afternoon I dropped by the local hospital to deliver a signed T-shirt to an Aussie supporter who was knocked down by a car two nights ago outside the team hotel. He broke an arm and both legs and is in a pretty sorry state. The authorities still don't know who was driving the car and I figure if I just lie low for another few days I should escape any charges.

There was some indecision over where to eat this evening, with a few of the lads pushing for Indian food, others wanting fish and chips while another group liked the sound of the pizza place round the corner. Warney said there was a bistro nearby he highly recommended so we were able to at least rule that one out. In the end we went the curry option.

After dinner we had a cocktail party hosted by the Australian press contingent. With so many journos around naturally I was pretty careful about what I said.

Todd Slams Team-mates!

Australian batsman Warwick Todd went on the attack at a team drinks function last night, labelling many of his team-mates as 'below par' and 'unfit to wear the Aussie cap'. Todd was also critical of the Australian team management, whom he described as 'a bunch of overpaid (continued on page 32 Sports Section)

DAY 46 JUNE 27

Australia vs. British Universities — Day 3

Nothing was said to me by the fellas on the bus this morning about the outrageous article that appeared in today's paper. This was because the team bus left without me. I managed to hitch a lift to the ground. Honestly, journalism in this country has hit an all-time low! Not only was I clearly speaking off the record last night, I was also clearly speaking off my face. Hopefully the whole thing will just blow over.

For the third day in a row the match was called off due to rain and everyone returned to the hotel to start the complex process of checking out. Over the years I've become pretty careful about examining the bill — it's amazing what hotels will try and slip past you — and today was no exception.

Pretty outrageous when you consider I never even used the laundry.

Today turned out to be a pretty special one for Warney with news that his wife Simone had given birth to a healthy baby girl. On the bus ride down to Southampton numerous crates of champagne were drunk and cigars smoked by all the lads in a true party atmosphere. And we hadn't even heard the news at this point, this was just a normal trip. However, arriving at the Grand Harbour Hotel Warney received a phone call from home telling him that everything had gone well, and that mother, daughter and sponsors where all doing fine. Of course, Warney's happiness was mixed with a tinge of regret at not being there for the birth of his first child but, as I explained to him, this is pretty standard for an international cricketer. I missed the birth of both my kids; the first time I was in India, the second I was

Oxford Moathouse

W. Todd, Room 217

Laundry —	£5.80
Telephone —	£8.43
Adult Video —	£17.00
Mini-bar —	£213.50
VAT —	£6.32
TOTAL:	£251.05

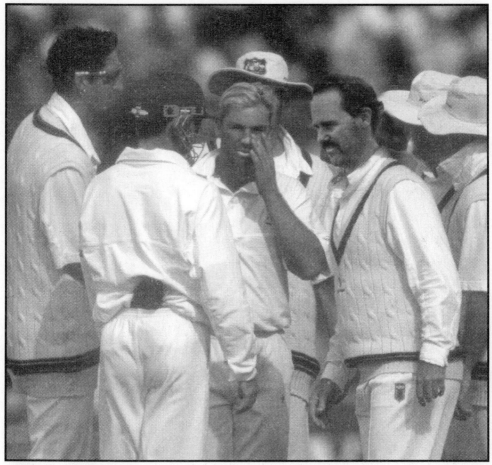

Yeah, yeah, another Warney wicket. Let's just get on with the game.

guest speaker at my district cricket club's awards night and couldn't afford to cancel as I'd already hired the tux. *Say la vee.*

After checking in there was a team meeting to discuss the tour thus far. Having lost the one-day series 3–0 and being one down in the Test series our captain Mark Taylor spoke about the need for us to all stand up and be counted, to be responsible for our own actions and not look to turn on each other with blame when things go wrong. It was a truly inspiring speech and a mark of Tubs' ability as a captain that he didn't have to name names for us all to know who he was referring to. I just hope Messrs Bevan and Waugh (S.) were paying attention.

DAY 47 | JUNE 28 | Australia vs. Hampshire — Day 1

Straight into another three-day match today. It's times like this when on tour that fitness becomes a key factor. I can't believe how sore I'm still feeling after the second Test, and that was over a week ago. I put it down to all that fast running between wickets and a few diving saves in the outfield. And that game of hoppo-bumpo we held in Blewie's room last night.

Thankfully I have a standard warm-up routine that sees me through even the busiest touring schedule:

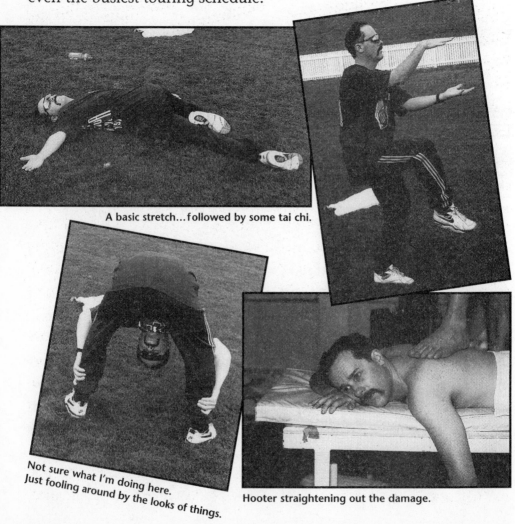

A basic stretch...followed by some tai chi.

Not sure what I'm doing here. Just fooling around by the looks of things.

Hooter straightening out the damage.

Hampshire won the toss and elected to bat on a pretty damp pitch — not such a smart decision as they crashed to be all out shortly after lunch for just 156 runs. Most notable failure was fellow Aussie Matt Hayden who, after surviving a dropped catch from yours truly, managed only 6 runs. Many feel Matt should have been part of the current Australian squad and he's certainly had a great season with Hampshire so far, but form deserted him today. Watching Hulkster trudge off the field I could tell he was pretty disappointed, as was I — I'd bet £75 on him to make a century.

Our openers got the Aussie innings off to a great start, before Herb fell for 61. Another wicket saw yours truly padding up and joining Tubs in the middle. Our skipper was approaching a half-century and told me to just take things easy, play myself in, no need to do anything rash. I middled the first ball I faced, dispatching it to the long on boundary for four. There's a funny sort of feeling you get as a batsman when you execute a stroke well early on, you just know it's going to be a big innings. So it came as something of a surprise when I was out hooking next ball.

Tubs is well known as a very attacking style of captain and for good reason. When he got back into the dressing-room at the tea interval he laid into me with a cricket stump. I can't really blame him. Getting out hooking is a pretty stupid thing to do. Not only have I let myself down but think of all the other guys who are depending on me. My manager, publicist, sponsors (corporate and merchandise), fitness adviser, the people at the Fine Pine Furniture Centre... and there's probably others I've forgotten.

By stumps we were 2 for 166, looking forward to a big score tomorrow. Apart from Tubs returning to form (53 runs, in about as many hours), the other big interest today was the unofficial 'bowl-off' between Kaspa and Dizzy. With room for only one in the next Test team it will be difficult to make a decision. In the end it may come down to fitness; Dizzy has an unfortunate tendency to break down during five-day games. In fact, he's known in some quarters as 'Leyland P-76', a reference to the legendary Australian car that, like Dizzy, was renowned for breaking down.*

Italian food tonight followed by yet another official engagement, drinks with the management of the hotel. Drinks functions like these can be a complete pain and, more importantly, a distraction from the real business of playing cricket. Fortunately the event ended early and we were all able to go out for a drink.

Back at the hotel I decided to phone Ros only to discover she'd put her back out. Fortunately Garry was over at the time and managed to get her into bed where she's now recovering nicely.

* I think I may have over-explained that.

DAY 48 JUNE 29

**Australia vs.
Hampshire — Day 2**

A nasty shock for Brendon Julian today. He received a call in the dressing-room informing him that his sister had been seriously injured in a car accident back in Australia. Understandably BJ was shattered and immediately began making arrangements to head home. It wasn't until after lunch that Tugga owned up to faking the phone call from an adjoining room.

There were plenty of smiles on field too as we continued to nail the Hampshire attack, advancing to 465 before declaring. Both Junior and Tubs made centuries and while I was naturally pleased for them it only served to make me more conscious of my own recent poor form. The team for the third Test is due to be announced in a few days and I'm pretty sure Bevan is after my spot. It's written all over his beady little face. Yesterday morning when I came down to breakfast he was sitting *directly* opposite Swampy, passing him jam and the ashtray and pretending to be interested in his cricket anecdotes. Little weasel.

To make matters worse I was officially informed at lunch that I had been reported yesterday to the match referee after it was *alleged*

Bat tossing is such a common feature of international cricket these days.

I threw my bat away as I was leaving the field. For goodness sake, bat tossing is such a common feature of international cricket these days you've got to wonder why the match referee even got involved. I guess the fact my bat hit his wife might have had something to do with it.

After a long day in the field there's nothing better than a hot shower, a good meal and an early night. So why I let the guys talk me into a skulling competition at the Southampton Arms remains a mystery. We eventually got back to the hotel around 3.00 am.

DAY 49 JUNE 30

**Australia vs.
Hampshire — Day 3**

As expected Hampshire crashed again today to be all out for just 176, giving us victory by an innings and 133 runs. According to some commentators it was our best win of the tour so far, although personally I wouldn't overlook our crushing first-up defeat of the Duke of Norfolk's XI. Admittedly that team had a few injuries, many of its top performers unable to play because of gout, but it was still a great victory. As was today. Naturally enough the boys celebrated pretty hard. Heals led us all in a rousing rendition of 'Under the Southern Cross', followed by various other traditional team victory songs. One of the most moving of these, only ever sung in the Aussie dressing-room after a win, goes like this:

'Aussie'

Aussie! Aussie! Aussie!

Aussieeeeeeeeeee Oy!

Oy! Oy! Oy!

Ausieeeeeeeeee!

(repeat chorus)

Copyright ACB. Reprinted by permission.

Of course it's hard to get the full effect without hearing the tune, but just reading these words is enough to send a tingle down the old Todd spine.

It was a great night and a welcome opportunity for me to take my mind off the fact that tomorrow the team for the third Test will be named. With so many of the boys now showing form there'll be a real tussle for the 11 places. It's at times like these I hate the way players start sucking up to Swampy, buying him drinks and hoping to grease their way into the team.

DAY 50 JULY 1

Up early this morning, taking Swampy a cup of tea in bed. Then it was on to the team bus for the trip to Manchester.

We checked into the Holiday Inn and unpacked our suitcases for what seemed like the one hundreth time on tour. My bags are in a sorry state, full of clothes that haven't seen an iron for quite some time. Which is odd, given the number of hotel irons I've pinched so far.

My new roomie is Glenn McGrath. Pigeon's a top bloke, and not at all what you'd expect from his 'country boy' image. For a start, he has a great love of literature. While the other guys are glued to the TV or video you'll more often than not find Pigeon curled up in the corner with his head buried in a pig-shooting magazine.

A heavy training session this afternoon during which Herb was given the terrible news that he'd been dropped from the team for the third Test. Given his excellent form thus far the big Victorian was quite understandably devastated. It wasn't until a few hours later when the Test squad was really named that he realised he'd been set up. The other guys with big smiles on their faces were Dizzy (who got the nod over Kaspa) and yours truly, who also made the squad.

At the team meeting tonight Swampy emphasised the need for match fitness and we could tell he was serious as he wasn't smoking at the time. I'm so keen to do well in this Test I even decided this afternoon to go off the grog. Didn't touch a drop until 7.30 tonight when the pre-match celebrations began in earnest.

Not that this is the first time I've taken the Pledge. A few years ago in West Indies after a Test I went three days without a drink. And you know what? I didn't even miss it. Possibly because I was unconscious for the entire period, having being struck by a Curtly Ambrose bouncer. Once discharged from hospital I more than made up for the break, and have been doing so ever since.

DAY 51 JULY 2

Not a great start to the day. Shortly after breakfast I was summoned by Crommo. Seems our tour manager's been on the blower to the ACB back in Sydney who are none too happy about an article I'd written for the Melbourne *Herald-Sun*. It was a humorous piece about English bowler Phil Tufnell in which I'd *jokingly* and *light-heartedly* called him a homosexual. Well the bureaucrats back in Sydney were claiming I'd breached ACB Standing Order No. 4, that a cricket player must 'not make comments which are considered detrimental to the interests of the game'. Give us a break, fellas! The article was not intended in any way to bring the game into disrepute — just Phil Tufnell. But as usual the ACB had already made up its mind and informed me I could look forward to a letter of reprimand and a fine in the next few days. At least I'll be getting some mail. Speaking of which, this letter arrived today.

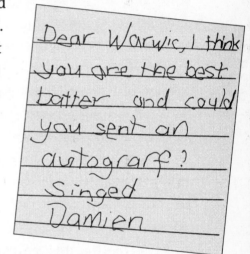

Dear Warwic, I think you are the best batter and could you sent an autograrf? Singed Damien

As usual, I left it to Gabe to reply:

EXCEL SPORTS MANAGEMENT
(Established 1995)

July 2, 1997

Dear Damien,

Mr Todd has asked me to write and inform you that he is far too busy concentrating on the current Ashes tour to be sending autographs. Kindly do not bother him with such a request again.

Yours sincerely,

G. Hirsh

G. Hirsh, Manager

The afternoon was spent training at Old Trafford. With training the day before a Test we always attempt to simulate as closely as possible actual match conditions. In the nets there's a lot of intimadatory bowling and verbal abuse, while back in the dressing-room we keep the CD player cranked up pretty loud.

Despite the intensity and seriousness there's always lighthearted moments and today was no exception. Lang was in the nets facing a couple of local bowlers when — ouch! — a quicker delivery struck him right in a very painful spot. Without going into details, let's just say it was his left testicle.

But on a more serious note Gilly was also injured at training, badly hurting his knee during a game of 'fielding soccer'. It was just one of those things, I guess. Five minutes earlier we'd all been playing Twister and everything was fine, then before you know it, Gilly's lying there with a torn medial ligament. It's a tough break for our reserve 'keeper, who has had only 14 minutes of first-class batting this summer. He'll have a scan tomorrow but if the verdict is as we expect — that he can no longer play golf — then he might as well go home now.

A 6.30 pm meeting brought the whole squad (minus Lang) together for a pre-Test run-through of the opposition's strengths and weaknesses. This is usually pretty detailed stuff involving videos and technical assessments like 'Atherton — likes to cut outside off-stump, keep the ball up'. Although I remember back in '93 the meetings started getting a little less serious after we kept winning every match. By the third Test it was just a case of AB naming a Pommy player, us all shouting 'girl!' and we'd be in the bar by 6.45.

DAY 52 | JULY 3

**3rd Cornhill Test,
Old Trafford — Day 1**

A big crowd was waiting at the ground this morning and, judging by the VB cans littering the playing surface, there was a fair Aussie contingent among them.

Before taking the field Tubs said a few words to us all. He told us that in his opinion winning was 90 per cent based on attitude, 10 per cent on technique and 10 per cent on determination. He's a cluey bloke Tubby, with a great cricketing mind. Maths has never been his strong suit.

A typical Aussie training session. Clockwise from top: We start with a bit of kick to kick...
watch Herb drop a few catches... a bit more footy... then head for the pub.

Tubs won the toss and elected to bat on a patchy-looking strip, a decision that soon backfired, with our skipper out in the third over for just 2. Obviously Tubs was pretty disappointed with himself as he walked off the field. We were all sitting upstairs in the viewing area and could hear him enter the dressing-room below. This was followed by the sound of a bat being thrown, several panes of glass being broken, and what appeared to be a retaining wall shifting backwards. All I could think was, wait until he discovers we've flushed his kitbag down the dunny.

The mood in our dressing-room became even more tense as Aussie wickets began to tumble. Eventually, at 3 for 42, it was crunch time for Warwick Todd. I took a deep breath, headed down the stairs and took that long walk over to the Ladbrokes tent. I don't like betting against Australia but this was too good to miss.

I came in a few overs later. Tugga was looking good on 63 and my role was simple; hold down one end, look for the ones and twos, and don't try anything rash. I was out hooking the second ball I faced.

Despite us ending the day at a pretty healthy 7 for 224 I was personally devastated at getting out to such a rash shot.

After a few drinks in the rooms the guys went out for a meal but I simply didn't feel capable of joining them. Largely because they wouldn't tell me where they were going. I also felt I needed time alone. I wish Ros was here. But then again, perhaps it's best she's not. I remember my first ever Test duck, back in Perth in 1990. I went home to Ros that night so wound up, so angry, I'm ashamed to admit that even blows were struck. Why she felt the need to hit me I've never worked out, but it was the last time I whinged to Ros about an on-field failure.

DAY 53 JULY 4

**3rd Cornhill Test,
Old Trafford — Day 2**

Coming down to breakfast this morning there was a pile of faxes waiting for me, all from fans back home. Most of them were quite spiteful and full of hate, accusing me of 'letting the team down'. Reading them all I was reminded of my grandmother and her wise old words 'if you can't say something nice about someone don't say anything'. I was reminded of Nanna because one of the nastiest faxes came from her.

Down at the ground play got away on time, with Tugga taking his overnight score to 108 before Gough disturbed his furniture. It was a magnificent innings and, combined with a quick-fire 31 from Pistol, took our first innings score to 235.

Butcher and Atherton opened as usual for the Poms and from the very first ball the pressure was on. Atherton fell cheaply to Pigeon but Butcher managed to play a few shots and started building a decent score. It was a classic Test battle; tense, full of pressure and relieved only by the occasional on-field quip. Honestly, the repartee that takes place out in the centre is a colourful and special part of the game. Heals calling stuff like 'Come on Warney, this guy's shittin' himself, I can smell it from here', a *bon mot* that invariably reduces us all to tears of laughter.

Mind you, this sort of quick-witted repartee is not confined to the field. I remember once in Perth walking back into the dressing-room after a dodgy lbw decision and throwing my bat down in anger. To my horror it bounced off a locker and hit Dean Jones. Without missing a beat Deano picked the bat up and, with a twinkle in his eye, hit me with it.

In the end it was Warney who broke through, taking five wickets and really tearing the Poms apart. He was ably assisted by Pigeon and Bev, who picked up the prized wicket of Butcher. Pistol was unlucky not to take a wicket, with many of his deliveries beating the bat. At times like this it's important for a paceman to keep believing in himself rather than saying 'I'm hopeless, I'm hopeless'. Leave those comments to the rest of us.

England ended the day 8 wickets down and still 70-odd runs behind. All in all a good day for Australia, the only 'sour' note being the dismissal of Graham Thorpe, run out under somewhat controversial circumstances. Now a lot of ill-informed b*#!shit has since been written about this incident by alleged 'experts', so perhaps it's time for someone to set the record straight. Here's a completely objective account of what happened:

Having struggled to reach 3 the overrated Pommy batsman (G. Thorpe) attempted a sucidal single during which he collided with a dashing and lightning-reflexed Australian fieldsman (me).

Now anyone who knows anything about cricket (and I think we can exclude the British press here) knows it is the *batsman's* responsibility to avoid the fieldsman. And the fieldsman's elbow.

Sadly, the incident cast a shadow over an otherwise enjoyable day's play and the Poms declined our invitation to join us for post-stumps drinks. Okay, Thorpe was in hospital, but the rest of them could have come. Personally I believe one thing that could truly improve this great game is the return of friendly interaction between teams after each day's play. The dressing-room is a place for both sides to come together over a few drinks, tell a few yarns, put aside on-field animosity. It's also a great place to listen to other players and learn. I remember chatting with the Poms back in '93 here at Old Trafford. We learnt that Robin Smith was having treatment on a hairline fracture of his big toe. Next day Merv came out, yorked him second ball and he had to be carried off the field.

DAY 54 | JULY 5 | 3rd Cornhill Test, Old Trafford — Day 3

Surprise surprise, the Pommy press have blown up yesterday's run-out incident, accusing us of 'unsportsmanlike behaviour' in not calling Thorpe back after he was given out. What would have been the point? He was unconscious. They went on to basically label the entire Australian side a bunch of cheats. Personally, I think you've got to be very careful with sweeping generalisations like that. No team can be branded as cheats, except of course the Pakis.

Fortunately we managed to put the controversy behind us and get on with wrapping up the Pommy tail, dismissing them early this morning for just 162. Then it was our turn to bat. As usual Tubs and Herb opened the innings and as usual Tubs was out cheaply caught in slips off a Headley out-swinger. He's nothing if not consistent. Blewie copped a pretty ordinary decision, being given out caught in slips off Croft when the cameras clearly showed the ball had bounced before Hussain took it. The scorecard should rightly read: **G. Blewett c Hussain b Croft** with the 'c' followed by the letters 'h.e.a.t.e.d' which, when combined, would form the word 'c.h.e.a.t.e.d'. Except you'd remove the full stops. Anyway, you get the idea.

With Junior out for a good half-century it was time for me to take the field. No one needed to remind me that this was a vital innings, not just for the team but for me personally. With so much batting talent knocking on the door I had to impress the selectors with a big knock. Sitting in the dressing-room I even went so far as to take out this diary and write myself a message: 'Compulsive hooking is just lazy. It's a careless option. Be strong, get into position early and play the percentage shots. You can do it!'

Those words were still ringing in my ears as I attempted to hook Headley, only to get a top edge and be dismissed for 3. I couldn't believe I fell for the trap! The English paceman dug one in short, I got inside it and...back to the pavilion. To be honest, the rest of the day went past in a bit of a blur. I sat in the rooms alone, watching Tugga battle his way towards another brave century. I stood and applauded as we reached stumps at 6 for 262. I partied back at the hotel. But really my heart just wasn't in it.

In the end I went back to my room, got out this diary and tried to put today's incident into some sort of perspective. But all I could write about myself was, 'You f#*kwit, you f#*kwit, you f#*kwit.'

(As I'm obviously still so upset about letting the team down today I asked my friend and current roomie Glenn McGrath to complete tomorrow's diary entry.)

DAY 55 | JULY 6

**3rd Cornhill Test,
Old Trafford — Day 4**

You f#*kwit, you F#*kwit, you f#*kwit, you f#*kwit, you f#*kwit, you f#*kwit, you f#*kwit, you f#*kwit, you f#*kwit, you f#*kwit, you f#*kwit, you f#*kwit, you f#*kwit, you f#*kwit, you f#*kwit, you f#*kwit, you f#*kwit you f#*kwit, you F#*KWIT!

DAY 56 JULY 7

**3rd Cornhill Test,
Old Trafford — Day 5**

Feeling a lot better. We declared yesterday at 8 for 395, setting the Poms 469 to win. Tugga made a brilliant 116, ably supported by Heals, Warney and Pistol. Then Dizzy got amongst the wickets, reducing the Poms to 5 for 130 by stumps. One of the many highlights of the day was the keeping of Heals, who had to contend with the spin of Bevan and Warney on a very unpredictable pitch. It got so bad that Heals actually had to don a helmet for only the second time in his career. (The first was at the WACA in '93 when Richie Richardson threatened to smash his head in after Heals sledged him.) The other difficulty we were forced to contend with was the constant pitch invasions by members of the crowd, nearly a dozen in all.

The match ended this morning in victory to Australia, with the Poms collapsing to be all out for 200. The last few wickets went to Pigeon

I know Greg Ritchie loves his cricket, but this is going too far.

Our wedding day. Believe it or not, Ros made all the dresses herself.

but the honours were definitely with Tugga who spear-headed our win with a century in both innings. He was a fitting Man of the Match.

Naturally there were a few quiet drinks in the dressing-room, followed by a few slightly noisier drinks back at the hotel. As usual Heals led the way with 'Under the Southern Cross', followed by a few other Aussie team favourites like 'True Blue', 'Khe Sahn' and the 'Macarena'. At around 10.00 pm I snuck off to phone Ros, as today is our ninth wedding anniversary. Such are the demands of modern sport I'm sad to say we've not spent one of them together. Twice I've been in England, once in Pakistan, and the other six times Ros has had netball practice.

To think it was nine years ago that we were married. I remember the day I met her like it was yesterday. It was my final year of school and I was in the nets training with the first XI, when this bunch of girls from St Stephanie's College walked by. I immediately noticed the brunette. She had this gorgeous smile, a casual, carefree walk and — even from a distance — a sensational body. Little did I realise that just two short years later I'd be marrying that girl's slightly frumpy best friend.

I phoned Ros from a quiet corner and she sounded breathless when she answered, almost panting. I figured out pretty quickly what she'd been up to. That bloody exercise bike! I warned her not to over-do it, before wishing her a happy anniversary. As it turned out, Ros had some rather exciting news: some guy from ABC Television had been ringing, wanting to get in touch with me. Apparently they want to do a story on me. She put them onto Gabe, who no doubt will have all the details.

A few more drinks with the boys and I was ready to call it a night. After five straight days of Test cricket and two batting failures I'd like to forget forever, it was time for some well-earned rest. Back in my room I was pleased to discover I'd received some more fan mail.

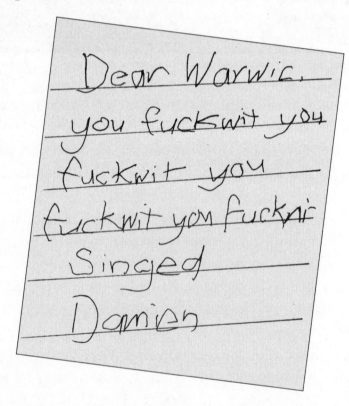

DAY 57 · JULY 8 — Australia vs Minor Counties XI

Details of our great win were all over the press this morning, along with some not so flattering photos of Warney skulling champagne and giving the crowd 'the finger' from the balcony at Old Trafford. Honestly, you'd think such a high-profile guy would learn to watch himself a bit more carefully in public. In my entire career I've only ever been photographed making an offensive gesture from the team balcony once, and even then I was careful to make sure you couldn't see my face.

As it happens, Warney left the squad today for a flying visit home to see his new daughter Brooke. This surprise departure raised a few eyebrows from those of us in the squad who believe you never leave a tour until the final ball

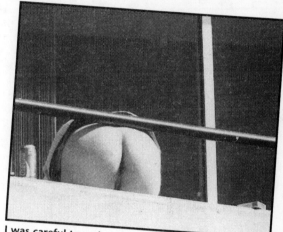

I was careful to make sure you couldn't see my face.

is bowled. The only exception would be for some genuine personal tragedy, like a sponsorship deal falling through or your manager quitting. But rushing off to see a new baby? I've known Test players who've had to be introduced to their kids at their fifth birthday party.

Anyway, the rest of us went straight into another tour match, a one-day affair against a Minor Counties XI at Jesmond. I knew this would be a valuable chance for me to show some form leading up to the next Test and I was pleased to see us win the toss and decide to bat first. Star of the Aussie innings was BJ, who knocked up a quick-fire 106, including 8 sixes and 9 fours. I'm pleased to say I also wielded the willow today with power, aggression and timing. I'm not so pleased to say pretty much all of this wielding took place in the Aussie dressing-room after I was given out lbw for 5.

I wielded the willow today with power, aggression and timing.

We went on to make 7 for 290, a target the home team failed to reach by just 9 runs. At these types of games we're inevitably obliged to stay for a drink or two, which can be a bit of a chore. After a drink or four things get a little better. By the time the home team kicked us out of their dressing-room at 2.30 am it had turned into quite a good night.

Returning to the hotel I received a call from Gabe. Turned out the ABC TV bloke chasing me was from *The Investigators*, some consumer watchdog show keen to ask a few questions about the sunglasses I was involved in marketing last year. It was a new range of fashion eye wear called 'Go-Glare', a nice little earner organised by Gabe. All I had to do was sign my name to an endorsement, wear the bloody things once or twice on the field and pick up the cheque. How were we to know the sunglasses didn't conform to Australian standards? The manufacturers in Taiwan assured us they were approved but it turns out they were only approved as a novelty item.

I was furious. As a high-profile sporting identity with a reputation to protect I have to be very selective about what I lend the name

Warwick Todd™ to. In the last ten years I've only ever endorsed a few select products: chewing gum, athletic footwear, those things old people kneel on in the garden, a range of non-stick aluminium cookware, one of the classier 0055 late-night telephone chat line services, the Fine Pine Furniture Centre and a new line of cattle drenches. That's it, more or less. So this Go-Glare fiasco came as a real shock. Naturally, as soon as we found out we were sitting on 60 000 illegal and potentially hazardous sunnies, we did the only decent thing and unloaded them to some wholesaler in New Zealand. But obviously a few slipped through the net and questions are now being asked.

Gabe said there's no need to panic but as a precautionary measure he'd like me to transfer all my assets into one of his shelf companies while he figures out what to do. To be honest, I don't need this sort of distraction. The fourth Test is only a fortnight away, I'm in the middle of a massive form slump and I still haven't even worked out whether I'm growing a beard.

DAY 58 JULY 9

Up early this morning for the bus trip to Edinburgh. Most of the guys sat up the front watching video highlights of last week's AFL round (aerial pingpong if you ask me), but I wasn't really in the mood. Frankly, I feel like I'm at the crossroads of my career. If I don't start making runs soon... Well, I don't want to even think about it. Stay positive Warwick, set yourself goals, one step at a time. Wasn't it Confucious who once said, 'A journey of a thousand miles begins with one small step for mankind'? Or maybe it was Neil Armstrong. Whatever. Keep your sights set on the next match.

Sister Reticulata prepares to select the team. That's me, front row right, about to get a clip across the ear.

And never forget the four 'D's' — Determination, Dedication, Drive and... I forget the fourth, but it's bloody important.

It's times like these I think back to all those years ago, as a kid, learning to play cricket at school under the steady guidance of my first female coach, Sister Reticulata.

Then of course there were the backyard 'Tests' I played with my brothers Phil and Graham and the other neighbourhood kids. We had an elaborate set of rules worked out:

1) One hand off the fence is out.
2) Over the fence is six and out.
3) If you're out first ball you're not out.*

Having systematically destroyed Mum's garden we eventually shifted our games to the street, where a new rule was introduced:

* Girls only.

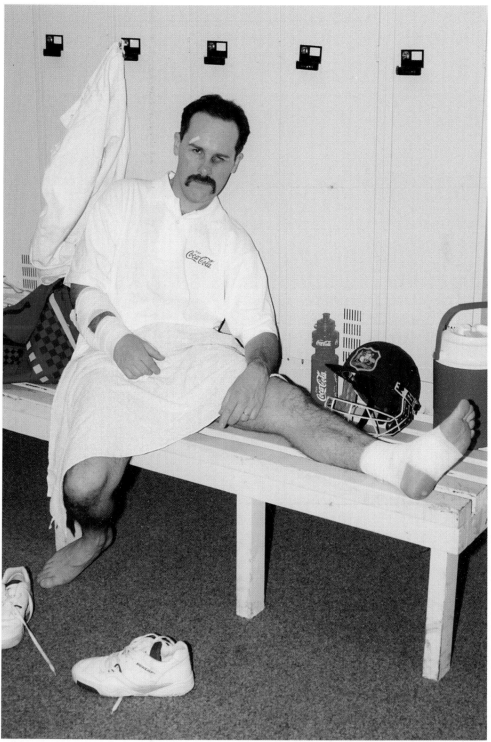

Edgbaston, June. Bruised and battered. It was after this that team management banned wrestling on the bus.

Shane Warne. (Head shown
smaller than actual size).

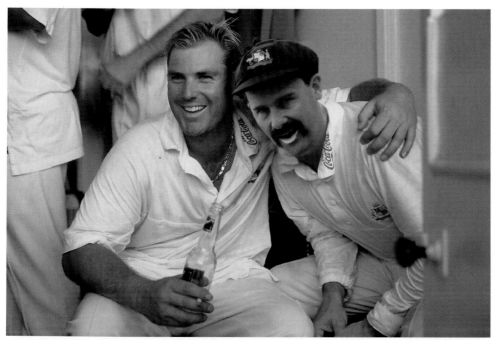

Warney and yours truly share a beer in the Aussie dressing room. Normally we players prefer to avoid physical contact but after a victory these rules are relaxed.

You never know when a member of the Australian Cricket Board will pop out with a word of encouragement.

In the rush to congratulate your bowler on a crucial wicket it's important you don't forget to give the batsman a decent send-off. 'Up yours Athers!'

I didn't take the catch but I did come up with the winning sledge.

4) The player facing oncoming traffic must call 'car' (we lived on a pretty busy road).

Of course, all of us playing back then dreamed of one day representing Australia, but as it turned out I was the only one who had the talent and commitment to achieve that goal. Phil became an accountant in Brisbane and Graham's spent most of his life in a wheelchair after an unfortunate breach of Rule 4. And I often ask myself 'Why?' Why has one person (me) gone all the way to the top while others (people other than me) have fallen short? I mean, forget about Phil and Graham (I did years ago) and ask yourself this: What is the difference between a good Shield player and a Test batsman? What's the difference between me and, say, Matt Hayden or Darren Lehmann? Why did the selectors say, 'Todd — he's in, a great player and a must for the Ashes squad. Hayden and Lehmann — losers.' Is it really as clear cut as that? I guess it must be.

By the time we made it to Edinburgh I was feeling a lot better about myself and joined the boys in sampling a few of the local whiskies. People rave about single-malt whisky but to be perfectly honest, I can't see what all the fuss is about. I tried Glenfiddich and Coke, Laphroig and Coke, Lagvullin and Coke — they all tasted much the same to me. Then it was time for dinner, followed by a karaoke session at the Dalmahoy Hotel, a few more whisky tastings, a tour of local nightclubs and then back to our rooms. After such a big day travelling, it was good to have a quiet night.

DAY 59 JULY 10

You'd think this far from Fleet Street we'd be safe, but I'm afraid now the Scottish press have jumped on the anti-Australian band wagon. A story appeared in this morning's local rag claiming several members of the Aussie team were last night refused admission to an Edinburgh nightclub after being deemed 'too drunk'! Sorry to ruin a good story fellas, but the truth of the matter is that Junior, Ponts and I were refused entry, but it was because the *guy we were with* was off his face. Now I'm not about to name that person here, his position as Australian coach is already shaky enough, but I wish just for once the press would give us Aussies a break.

With only a light training session scheduled for this afternoon I decided to take the opportunity for a little shopping. One of the great things about travelling overseas is that you can always bring the family back a special memento or souvenir of the places you've been. I've already got something for Ros — a litre bottle of duty-free Kahlua — but I still need something for the girls. I have two daughters, who are seven and nine. Being children of a famous sports star (me), Ros and I have worked hard to ensure they both keep their feet on the ground. You see some high-profile parents do terrible things to their kids: shower them with presents, give them ridiculous pretentious names, all sorts of stuff. Hopefully we've managed to avoid that with Brialanna and Raleisha-May.

I got back to the hotel just in time for one of my weekly media commitments, phoning through a report for the *Komedy Klub* breakfast radio show. However, speaking off-air to the producer, she told me it's now called the *All New Komedy Klub* after one of them quit and then slapped an injunction on the others using the original name. So before doing my report they got me to record a new promo: 'Hi, I'm Aussie cricketer Warwick Todd and you're listening to Slurps, TJ and Dannielle on the *All New Komedy Klub* on 4MB-FM.' The producer then put me on hold while they waited for the song to finish. My new roomie Junior was watching TV in the corner at the time and I suddenly came up with a hilarious idea. Why don't I get him to do the report, pretending to be me? We can tell them at the end, and it'll be a real hoot. I quickly ran the idea past Junior who's on for a stir and, with 20 seconds to go, he grabbed the phone. Now Junior's had very little media experience and I figured he'd be caught out within about 10 seconds, but to my surprise he started chatting and chatting and chatting. My reports normally run about two minutes; Junior was on the phone for six, telling jokes and stories about the tour. Eventually he tells them the truth, it's Mark Waugh not Warwick Todd, and I can hear a fair bit of laughter through the phone. Got 'em!

DAY 60 | JULY 11

Another day off. Boredom can be a big factor on a long tour such as this. You have to constantly come up with ways of filling in your spare time. You could train, I guess, but you don't want to take the edge off your cricket.

I was just about to get out of bed and go downstairs for lunch when the phone rang. It was Gabe with some big news. The *All New Komedy Klub* now want *daily* Ashes reports. 'Great!' I say. 'Not great,' says Gabe. 'They want them from Mark Waugh.'

To make matters worse I suddenly realised I was running late for a talk at some local school. This is something I used to do quite a bit of back home, until an unfortunate incident put a cloud over the whole thing. I don't particularly want to go into details, let's just say it involved a speech at a primary school in Adelaide in which it was *alleged* I was drunk. All right, I admit I'd had a few but I was perfectly in control. And you know what? If I was invited back again I'd say exactly the same things. Maybe less use of the magic word.

The other work with kids I really enjoy is coaching. Whenever we tour overseas we try to run clinics in underprivileged areas — India, Pakistan, earlier this year it was South Africa. That was a real eye-opener for me, seeing first-hand the damage years of apartheid had caused. The black population of the little township we visited near Bloemfontein was living in total squalor, no one in the squad had seen anything like it (except for the blokes from Queensland). But you know what? What these kids lacked in wealth they more than made up for with enthusiasm. There was no pitch, no nets and their only equipment was an old-looking bat and half-a-dozen ancient leather balls, yet I conducted one of the most rewarding coaching clinics I've ever held. Talk about keen! I faced up to a couple of young would-be fast bowlers who in their excitement kept making the fundamental mistake of pitching the ball hopelessly full. Each time this happened I'd step down the 'pitch' and hoik it over the fence and into a nearby sewerage channel. By the time every ball they owned had been swept off down the drain, I think they'd all been taught a valuable cricketing lesson.

Despite the sub-standard facilities these South African kids were forced to play with, I saw real talent there. It may take a few years, but I dream of the day some young black kid comes up to me during a Test match and tells me he was at that clinic all those years ago. As long as it's not the little shit who stole my camera.

I eventually made it to the school where it turned out they wanted me to address the entire school assembly! I don't mind talking to small class groups but I absolutely loathe the idea of speaking to such a big crowd. I really had no idea what to say. 'Just speak about yourself,' suggested the headmaster. Well, how I got through those three and a half hours I'll never know. But somehow the words just seemed to flow.

Back at the hotel there was a team meeting called to discuss the claim we're having too many meetings. No real resolution and we agreed to hold another meeting about the issue tomorrow.

DAY 61 JULY 12

Australia vs. Scotland

With rain predicted and a bitter wind blowing we weren't surprised to find a fairly small crowd waiting at the ground. I must say, playing international cricket you get to see every extreme. Here in Edinburgh today there were probably 300 spectators. Just last year we were playing a World Cup semi-final against the West Indies in Chandigarh in front of a crowd estimated to be made up of 70 000 people. From at least a dozen different families.

Speaking of that World Cup semi-final, I'm often reminded of this bloke we had as our room attendant, a little Indian guy called Rajendra. Like so many Indians Rajendra lived in pretty extreme poverty, but dreamed of one day buying a block of land for himself and his family. It would have cost him about $1000 which he was never going to make, and so that night after our miraculous win all the boys had a whip-around and presented Rajendrea with a plastic bag containing $800. He was so overwhelmed that he was crying and bowing and carrying on. We later heard he went out and bet the lot on Australia to win the final. I'm told he's now a street beggar in Bombay.

Apart from different sizes, the other thing you've got to get used to is how different crowds react. Pommy spectators tend to be fairly reserved. The Pakis are probably the most vocal. They scream, throw things, set fire to stands. And they don't drink! Imagine what these people would be like with a belly full of beer? Australians, I guess.

We won the toss and elected to bat but there was drama before the first ball was even bowled with news that Slats might not be able to take the field because of severe vomiting. Someone had chucked all over his kitbag. Fortunately another set of whites were found and the gritty opener took his place in the centre, where he compiled a classy 95. I managed to score just 14 before being involved in a stupid run-out with BJ. It was a silly mix-up and there's nothing to be gained going back over the details here,* or debating whose fault it was.**

Today's lunch was chicken and it pretty much summed up the morning's play; cold, tough and uninteresting. As it turned out the match was abandoned soon after lunch due to rain.

The only positive aspect of my brief innings was the discovery that someone had put Dencorub on the inside of my protector. Even though the pain was intense I was relieved to know the boys had obviously forgiven me for failing at Old Trafford. Being the victim of a cruel practical joke was all the proof I needed that I was 'back in the team'.

As usual there were a few quiet drinks in the dressing-room after the match. During this time an elderly gentleman called Des Tavistock was brought into our rooms. Des is from Sydney, he's 78 years old and totally blind, yet he has followed every match of the tour so far. You might ask why a blind person would bother actually travelling to the grounds, but according to Des, being there helps him feel more part of the occasion.

The old Dencorub on the protector trick.

Des is a true cricket fan and an inspirational example of someone overcoming adversity. He had a lot of stories to tell about past tours but to be perfectly honest, he was becoming a little tedious. To get rid of him we pretended we all had an official function to attend. (Please, no one ever read this paragraph out to him.)

* BJ pushed a ball towards mid-off, it was his call, I had my back to the fielder and trusted his judgment, he was wrong, I was caught a metre short through no fault of my own and he bloody well knows it.

** It was BJ's.

DAY 62 | JULY 13

After a traditional Scottish breakfast (two Egg McMuffins), it was out to Edinburgh airport for the flight back to London. Needless to say we weren't travelling light, with every player by now carrying a bulging coffin as well as personal gear. By the time everything was loaded it turned out our plane was too heavy to take off and we were told that excess baggage would have to be left behind. It was a strange feeling saying goodbye to Ponts and BJ in the departure lounge, but we knew they'd catch up with us down south.

Having touched down in London it was onto the bus for the trip up to Middlesex. As we're now two months into the tour wives and girlfriends are officially allowed to join us, and there was quite a welcoming party outside the Excelsior Hotel. Of course I knew Ros wouldn't be there, she's got her hands full at home. And in many ways I'm glad. You see, I think the presence of wives/girlfriends can have a negative effect on a touring squad. Guys don't want to go out partying together as a team so often, there's a lot less drinking and no one wants to wrestle on the bus any more. Despite these misgivings it was good to see the ladies and that night Tubs made a heartfelt speech about the major role our wives and girl-friends play in our cricket careers. It was a touching tribute to our better halves and a real pity they couldn't be there to hear it, but under ACB rules the team hotel is off-limits to the ladies until the final two weeks of tour.

Ros enjoying a county match in '93. Wives and girlfriends get just as much of a thrill out of an Ashes tour as we do.

DAY 63 JULY 14

Australia vs. JP Getty XI

Today's game was in Buckinghamshire at the private estate of J Paul Getty, an eccentric American billionaire who is so cricket-mad he foots the bill for the entire event. And it turned out to be a great day, with the celebrity-studded crowd (including Mick Jagger) treated to some fine batting and bowling from both teams. The match was played in a friendly atmosphere that harked back to the days when cricket was truly amateur. It was sort of like playing in Tasmania.

The only sour note was news that former Windies batsman Keith Arthurton pulled out of the home team when he learnt he wasn't going to be paid. This was very short-sighted of Keith — he should

We Aussie cricketers play a lot of charity matches and one woman synonymous with charity was, of course, Mother Teresa. I had the privilege of meeting her in Calcutta during the '96 World Cup. This inspirational woman shuffled up, looked me in the eye and said something I've never forgotten: 'How's Warney's finger?'

have realised that on charity days like this it doesn't matter whether or not you get money. We managed to stash enough crates of Getty's Veuve Cliquot on the team bus to more than make up for the lack of match payments.

On-field highlights included Herb's 95 off just 101 balls and opposition skipper Martin Crowe's equally impressive 115 not out. I contributed a solid 37, a knock that should impress the selectors, though of course unofficial games like today's are not really a true guide to form. Yes, Slats went for just 10 and Ponts made a duck but I really don't think these FAILURES should be taken into account when it comes time to select the team for the fourth Test. Sure, they both FAILED but FAILING in a game like today's should not be taken as any true indication that SLATS or PONTS may FAIL again in a genuine first-class match.

Back at the hotel tonight we had a quick team meeting before heading to the pub where we were visited by a group of Australian cricket fans who have been following the Ashes tour since it began. One of these cricket devotees, a mad-keen supporter called Craig Gibbs from Cronulla actually went so far as to hand me an entire diary describing their various adventures on tour. He knew I was compiling a tour diary and thought a few excerpts from his might make an interesting addition. I thanked him and promised to think about the idea, but to tell the truth his stuff was pretty boring so I've decided not to use it.

The Pommy press have got onto the fact that a lot of the guys' wives and girlfriends have joined the tour but are not staying at the team hotel. On the 1993 tour they mockingly referred to this situation as the 'Aussie sex ban', which is quite ridiculous. No one's ever said to any Aussie player he can't have sex for the first six weeks; just not sex with his wife or girlfriend. And it makes good sense. You want every member of the squad focused on the tour. As I've said before, I support it and so does Ros. Enthusiastically.

DAY 64 JULY 15

Up early this morning for a photo session with Community Aid Abroad. I'm a 'Good-Will Ambassador' for the organisation and have been involved with them for almost ten years. It began with Ros and I sponsoring a little Vietnamese child whose life has no doubt been improved by our regular monthly donation of $30.* Shortly after, CAA asked me to visit one of their aid projects in Bangladesh. As a Test cricketer I've travelled the world and seen some pretty terrible sights, (the memory of Arjuna Ranatunga in the showers still haunts me), but this trip to Bangladesh was a complete eye-opener. The people living in the little village we visited had no running water, no doctors and they survived on just a few handfuls of rice a day. After experiencing poverty like that first hand I made a promise to never again complain about things we take for granted back home.

Breakfast was late again today. You'd think if a hotel offers room service they'd at least have enough staff to bring the bloody meals up. To make matters worse, there was an article in the *Star* this morning suggesting I'd been rude and abusive to a local journo during a phone interview the previous day. Now I'll admit we had something of a heated exchange, but in his story this guy neglected to mention one minor detail about the interview — it was 7.05 in the bloody morning! I think anyone's got a right to be a little shirty when they're asked stupid questions at that time of the day. Looking back on the incident I don't even know why I rang him.

It really annoys me how often journos 'beat up' the facts to get a good story. Many years ago I was accused of 'outrageous behaviour' during a Shield match against South Australia. What happened was I used to be quite a useful seamer at that level and during one particular spell I had the batsman plumb lbw on numerous occasions.

*Tax-deductible.

Not that the umpire saw it that way, giving each of my appeals the thumbs down. Anyway, I finished my last over and went to grab my jumper from the umpire. Then, at the last minute, I decided I didn't need it and told him to hang onto it. That's it, simple as that. Hardly sounds like 'outrageous behaviour' does it? Asking an umpire to hang onto your jumper. My exact words may have been something more along the lines of 'stick the jumper up your arse', but let's not get bogged down in semantics. Next thing I know some talentless hack from the *Advertiser* is accusing yours truly of 'outrageous behaviour'. Before I knew it the entire media pack had jumped on board and I was blasted in the press for days. Classic case of 'trial by media'. What really got my goat was that the ACB had a procedure in place for dealing with on-field behaviour, it wasn't the place of some newspaper non-entity to demand action. As it happens, the umpire did see fit to report me and I was ordered to front the Board which fined me $1000. And another $1000 when I told them to stick it up their arses. But the point is, the whole thing would never have been such a big deal if the press hadn't stuck its big nose in.

The Pommy crowds have always responded well to my good-natured antics.

A light training session this afternoon saw me middling the ball pretty well. So much of cricket is a confidence game and I'm confident I can do well in tomorrow's tour match. Back at the hotel there was a team meeting in which new arrival Darren Berry* was officially welcomed. Plumb** is here to replace the injured Gilly as our reserve wicket-keeper, although to tell the truth I can't see Heals ever being injured badly enough to miss a game. Over the years I've

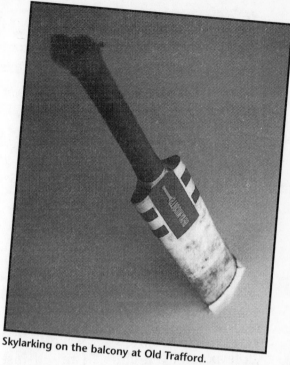

Skylarking on the balcony at Old Trafford.

seen our number-one 'keeper play with a broken thumb, dislocated fingers, torn cartilages. The only time I can remember us seriously thinking about not having him behind the stumps was in '95 in the Windies when he developed tonsilitis and couldn't talk.

After the meeting a few of the guys started planning a big night out but I settled for a room-service dinner, chicken and soup, along with a chilled bottle of Australian chardonnay. To my horror the total came to £23. I almost felt guilty signing Michael Slater's name on the bill.

* Yet to be nicknamed.

** Until now.

DAY 65 JULY 16

**Australia vs.
Glamorgan — Day 1**

By this stage of the tour, non-playing members of the squad are no longer obliged to attend all matches and so the team for today's game is down to 13 players. The remaining four blokes have been given time off to spend with their wives or girlfriends. Or, if they prefer, someone else's wife or girlfriend.

There's little doubt that one of the hardest roles on a long tour such as this is that of 'extra', being a member of the squad who rarely gets to play but is expected to turn up at most of the matches and provide support to the on-field players. I'm very conscious of how frustrating and demoralising such a role can actually be and, as a senior player, I go out of my way to make sure our 'extras' feel a valuable part of the team. It might just be the odd word of support or, occasionally, finding them little tasks that give them some sense of worth. So imagine my surprise this morning when Justin Langer refused to go pick up my dry-cleaning! You just can't help some people.

Unfortunately Glamorgan fielded a pretty weak team today, omitting Waqar Younis, Robert Croft and Steve Watkin after they all *allegedly* failed 'fitness tests'. Jeez this makes my blood boil. Never in my entire career have I resorted to this tactic; I'm proud to say every time I've failed a fitness test it's been 100 per cent legitimate. Honestly, what's the point of us showing up to these county matches if they're going to involve second-rate teams? As one local scribe was prompted to write, 'If county tour matches continue in this fashion we'll soon need barbed-wire fences to keep the spectators in!' (This of course being a twist on the normal situation in which barbed-wire fences are used to keep spectators out, rather than in.*)

Anyway, the Glamorgan 'Second XI' won the toss this morning and sent us in to bat. Everyone got amongst the runs, even Tubs, but

*I think I may have over-explained that.

most interest was on the 'battle' between Ponts, Slats, Lang, Bev and myself. We're all basically pushing for the one Test berth and on today's form no one really ruled themselves out. I guess Ponts was a little scratchy round the off-stump and Lang played and missed a little more often than you'd like from a potential Test batsman. Slats is of course only just an opener and Bev's

Trying out new beard, July 1997.

obviously out of the race so, looking at things objectively, you'd have to say I'm still the obvious choice. But we'll just have to wait and see.

We declared at 369 and sent the home team in. Despite some spirited bowling from Kaspa and Pistol the Glamorgan boys made it to stumps without loss.

As is customary we were obliged to share a few quiet drinks with the opposition team after play, before returning to the Copthorne Hotel for a few more non-obligatory drinks. Warney's yet to rejoin the squad but even several thousand kilometres away he's still making headlines. Apparently our Sheik of Tweak's got a new book due out soon entitled *My Own Words*, in which he (and whoever they found to insert the verbs) describes the Poms as 'soft'. Big mistake, Warney. You should never criticise your opposition, it only strengthens their resolve. That's why when I'm writing or speaking in public I make sure I only ever bag Australian players.

DAY 66 JULY 17

Australia vs. Glamorgan — Day 2

Outside the hotel this morning there was the usual group of English fans hanging round, all desperate for an autograph. I gave my usual blanket 'sorry but no' and was about to get on the bus, when out of the corner of my eye I spotted an old guy in a wheelchair holding up a tattered autograph book. He looked like he'd been waiting for hours so I decided to make an exception. I went over and said 'sorry but no' to him personally.

Thanks to an inspired spell of bowling from Pistol (5 for 61) we were able to wrap up the Glamorgan innings this morning for just 254. Bev and Kaspa also took a few wickets, with BJ our only bowler to miss out. But as I said to the big West Australian at lunch, 'Mate, you can sometimes bowl well and not take a wicket — that often happens in cricket. No doubt fate will even things up one day when you take four or five wickets by bowling poorly. And, knowing you BJ, I'm sure that day will be soon.' I think he felt a lot better after hearing this.

After lunch we set about building on our first innings lead. It was a good session, marred only by one incident involving the Glamorgan team and myself. I was on 17, facing Dale, when I clipped a ball to midwicket. Ponts called 'Yes!' and we scrambled through for a rather ambitious single. Cosker shied at the stumps as I was nearing my crease and the ball clipped my left foot, deflected away from the wicket (a wicket it was never going to hit anyway) and rolled out towards fine leg. This allowed me to complete the run. And two others. Well, did the home team go off their collective nuts! You'd think I had deliberately reached out and kicked the ball, rather than simply been the victim of a poor throw. And besides, the shot I'd played was heading into the outfield so it was more or less fitting that the ball ended up there. But try telling the Glamorgan boys that. For the next three overs I was subjected to a stream of abuse, spewed at me from behind the stumps. The filthy tirade was unsportsmanlike, unnecessary and, for the most part, untrue.

Needless to say, I was pretty shaken. Even more so when I was dismissed a few runs later by one of the worst lbw decisions ever made in first-class cricket. The ball would have been lucky to hit first slip! However, I'm an Australian sports-man, I'm very conscious that some-where out there there's a kid with a poster of me on his wall. Possibly signed. Possibly by me. So there was no anger, no violent outbursts on the field. But jeez did I tear that dressing-room apart. I'm told they still haven't been able to remove my bat from the wall where I shoved it through.

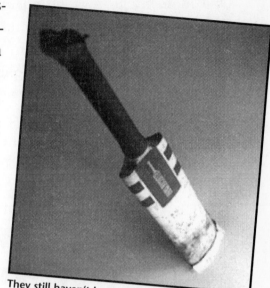

They still haven't been able to remove my bat.

Now anyone who's played cricket with me knows me as a bloke who loves to join the boys in the dressing-room for a pot or two after a match. But not tonight. For a start there was no furniture left standing. And besides, after being dismissed so unfairly like that you just don't feel like sitting round at the ground drinking. I went back to the hotel to do that.

DAY 67 JULY 18

**Australia vs.
Glamorgan — Day 3**

We lost Junior in the first over this morning. No idea where he went. One moment he was sitting in the dressing-room, the next he'd wandered off muttering something about 'a hot tip in the fourth'.

Tubs pulled the pin at 7 for 217, leaving Glamorgan to make 333 off 58 overs. Predictably the home team put up the shutters, inching their way to 3 for 211 when the game was mercifully called off.

Back at the hotel we had some interesting news. Apparently the entire England team will be attending a 'motivational camp' tomorrow in preparation for the fourth Test. If you ask me this sort of exercise is a waste of time and only goes to show that the Poms must be a little worried about their form. From memory they had one of these camps before the series began and it involved ridiculous 'bonding' exercises

The media have enormous power to convey the drama and excitement of international cricket. This is an abuse of that power.

like driving Range Rovers round blind-folded. What's the big deal? There's not a member of the current Australian squad who hasn't driven home blind. We don't need 'motivational camps' to help us do that.

After dinner the boys went out for a few drinks but to be perfectly honest my heart wasn't in it. Just the thought that I might not be named in the next Test 11 was making me feel sick. It got so bad that at one point I almost got up and left the pub early. Of course, this sort of negative thinking is very unlike W Todd. Anyone who knows me knows I'm normally an optimist. To me the beer glass is never half empty — it's always half full. You should have seen Ponts tonight, strutting round buying drinks like he knew the Test berth was his. Well let me tell you, sunshine — the battle's not over yet. Warwick Todd doesn't give in that easy. I'm a fighter. I've always been a fighter. Back in 1991/92 when I won the car as Player of the Series and AB insisted I donate it back to the team, I fought him. And I'll fight for my place in this team. There's still one tour match to go, there's still one more chance to show the selectors what I'm made of and I'm bloody well going to get out there and do it!

DAY 68 | JULY 19 | Australia vs. Middlesex — Day 1

Today's match began well with Middlesex choosing to bat on a slow wicket. The only sour note was an unfortunate run-in between myself and Glenn McGrath. It was in the fifth over. Pigeon got one to beat the bat of Middlesex's Pooley and Heals let fly with a (fairly optimistic) appeal. To be honest, I don't know where my mind was but I failed to join in the appeal. My fault, no argument. The rule has always been quite clear: when Heals goes up we all go up. (No wonder fielding can be so tiring.) The appeal was turned down and I could tell Pigeon blamed me.

Fortunately this only seemed to fire our bowlers up and we got through the Middlesex openers fairly cheaply. But their captain Mark Ramprakash dug in and was looking set to build a big score. Despite

The rule has always been quite clear: when Heals goes up we all go up.

a few bowling changes and some imaginative field placings we couldn't budge him. That's when Heals weaved his magic. Standing up to the stumps our 'keeper whispered a few pleasantries that had the little part-curry-muncher fuming. Heals called him 'gundoo', which I'm told is Indian for poofta. Our wicket-keeper's so experienced he can actually sledge in four different languages. He knows Afrikaans for arsehole (*kruzenfrorg*), Urdu for cheat (*malik*) and enough offensive expressions to bluff his way through just about every island in the West Indies. The tactic worked and Ramprakash holed out for 76.

Of course, not everyone appreciates the subtleties of finely honed verbal harrassment. During the summer of 1996/97 West Indies legend Brian Lara went so far as to officially complain. As usual the press jumped on this and beat it up. But let me now put the situation into context, without all the emotion and ill-will. For a start, Lara's always been up himself. He struts into the country and all we hear is '375, 375'. I don't care how many centimetres a bloke's penis is, let's see him perform at the crease. Well, it didn't happen for old Brian that summer. Real form slump. Naturally the crowd let him know it. Things came to a head during a one-dayer at the MCG in December when Lara was facing up to Moody. Certain uneducated onlookers started a chant: 'Lara is a wanker, f#*k off Lara'. I told our slips cordon to knock it off but they kept going, and I gotta hand it to them, it worked — Lara departed for 5.

By the end of the day we had Middlesex all out for 305. Tomorrow will be my chance to bat.

DAY 69 | JULY 20

**Australia vs.
Middlesex — Day 2**

Our openers made solid progress with Herb racing to 83, followed by good knocks from Blewie and Junior. It was a particularly good innings from Junior given he was struck a nasty blow in the groin early in proceedings. I can tell you, as a batsman there's nothing guaranteed to break your concentration quicker than a cricket ball to the gonads. Seeing Junior out there doubled over in pain reminded me of probably my worst experience of on-field agony. It was in South Africa when I was struck by a scorching Allan Donald delivery that hit my protector side on and shifted the 'family jewels' about six inches back. Fair dinkum, I felt like the old 'goolies' were about to explode. I bent double with pain — it was like a vice was tightening round my 'niagras' — and barely managed to negotiate the remaining overs before lunch. Back in the rooms a quick examination of the old 'jatz crackers' revealed a set of severely swollen 'nuts'. Hooter packed my 'bollocks' in ice and sent me off to a urologist at the Durban hospital who diagnosed a 'peripheral haematoma' or, in layman's terms, 'bruised balls'. There was also the possibility of blood clotting and I was told that if the swelling failed to go down over the next month I may have to lose a 'knacker'. Fortunately things settled down and the Todd cods remained intact. Funnily enough though, to this day I still feel the odd twinge of pain in the 'orchestra stalls' and can't stand Ros touching me there. Which is just as well — she can't stand touching me there either.

But I digress. Back to the game and the only Aussie to really fail today was Ricky Ponting, a.k.a. Ponts, a.k.a. Punter, a.k.a. R. PONTING C. SHAH B. TUFNELL 5.

Certainly won't do his selection chances any good.

I came in late in the day. With fading light and the ball moving round quite a bit it was not the situation any batsman struggling for form really wants. But I kept my head down, refusing to take any

I was seeing the ball really well.

risks and — with just a few overs before stumps — found myself on 36. To be honest I felt pretty confident, especially as I was seeing the ball really well. I certainly saw it come off an inside edge and shatter my stumps. Still, 36 runs — that's 31 more than Ponts.

Highlight of the day was undoubtedly Junior's innings, the nuggetty New South Welshman ending play with an unbeaten century. Watching on from the Lord's dressing-room we enjoyed a few drinks as he hammered the Middlesex attack, toasting him generously on his way to the magic three figures. At stumps we all agreed a standing ovation was called for, and we would have given him one had we been able to stand.

After dinner tonight a few of the guys were planning to go for a few drinks at London's Planet Hollywood but with another day still to play I announced I'd be having a quiet night in.

DAY 70 | JULY 21 Australia vs. Middlesex — Day 3

Woke this morning with a massive headache. Think I must have sampled every cocktail on the Planet Hollywood list. Eventually made it down to breakfast and onto the bus.

We declared this morning at 7 for 432 (Junior 142 not out) and our bowlers immediately set about knocking over the Middlesex line up. Warney picked up two wickets in his first eight balls and things were looking good until the fifth over when Kaspa got a beautiful outswinger to beat the bat of Gatting and Heals took a magnificent diving catch low down to his right. Imagine our surprise when the former England captain refused to walk! Next thing we know the square leg umpire's come in and tells Heals that the ball was not gloved cleanly. Heals of course said 'yes it was' but the appeal was refused. In effect, he was accusing our wicket-keeper of cheating! Now let me state for the record right here and now, I've known Ian Healy for the best part of ten years and I can tell when he's cheating. There's a certain look in his eye, I've seen it hundreds of times. And that catch was legitimate, end of story.

After this unfortunate incident Middlesex pretty much put up the shutters, stuggling to 6 for 201 when the match ended, a fairly lame draw.

After a few drinks with the home team it was onto the bus for the trip to Leeds. It should have taken just over an hour but, thanks to an IRA bomb threat, traffic had to be completely diverted. Having eventually checked in at the hotel we decided to hold another fines meeting, our second of the tour. These are a bit of an Aussie team tradition and they're a great way to get team spirit going. Unfortunately this one turned ugly, with the committee accusing Bev of crying during a bus trip when we screened a video of *Sleepless In Seattle*. Bev insisted he wasn't crying, his eyes were just watering because of the smoke from Warney's cigarette. Warney replied that at least his smoke smelt better than Lang's BO. Lang snapped back that Warney and his mates wouldn't know the first thing about sweat, having not lifted a finger since they arrived. From there things really turned ugly with an all-in fist fight only narrowly being averted by Tugga bursting in to anounce it was happy hour in the main bar. We might put a hold on the next fines meeting.

Lying in bed tonight I struggled to sleep. Thoughts about the up-coming Test and whether I'd be picked kept rattling round in my head. To give you some sort of idea, this was the kind of 'internal conversation' I was having:

TODD:	Let's face it, you're going to be dropped.
SUBCONCIOUS:	They haven't picked the team yet mate.
TODD:	But I failed again. And Ponts made a ton.
SUBCONCIOUS:	When?
TODD:	Against Glamorgan.
SUBCONSCIOUS:	Ponts is a flash in the pan. You've got the runs on the board.
TODD:	Tour average of 35.4.
SUBCONCIOUS:	And you haven't played every match.
TODD:	Another beer?
SUBCONCIOUS:	My shout.

DAY 71 JULY 22

Up early this morning and off to the gym. While my fitness levels have been sufficient for the past few county games, I know that a Test takes a lot more out of you. You can't go into five nights of drinking underprepared.

The England team was announced this morning, with no real surprises. Our main interest focused round their fast bowler Dean Headley, who was declared fit despite a recent side strain. I must say the English bowling this summer has been quite impressive, with Headley and especially Gough both giving us plenty to go on with. Mind you, neither speedster is up there with our boys for pace or fire. I'm often asked 'Which country has the most difficult bowlers to face?' Tough question for me because I handle them all so well. I'd probably have to say the West Indies. Without being in anyway racist it's a fact that picking the red ball up out of a black hand is very tough. This, combined with the fact that so many of them are cheats.

After the gym workout I went for a beard trim before heading back for morning tea.

Then came the announcement that was to change my life.

Back at the hotel the team for the fourth Test was announced. And the name W. Todd was missing. In stunned silence I went through the names again and again. Still no Todd. A range of emotions swept over me. Anger — I'd just spent 15 minutes on the exercise bike. Disbelief — I've been part of the side for 12 years. I guess the other guys knew how I'd be feeling because they all kept out of my way. At a sponsor's golf day. Suddenly there was a hand on my shoulder. It was Swampy. He suggested we go back to his room for a chat. To tell the truth, I let him and Crommo do most of the chatting. I just sat and listened.

Swampy began by saying he and the other selectors still believed in me and that there was definitely a place for me in the team. Same speech they once gave Dean Jones. Crommo chimed in, claiming it was purely a question of form and that the ACB were 100 per cent behind me. But I knew for a fact those bureaucratic mates of his back in Australia had been questioning my 'mental stability' for quite some time. (It's amazing what you can learn going through the faxes in someone's wastepaper basket.) I put this to Crommo and he became quite hostile, dragging up all sorts of incidents from my past, including my suspension from grade cricket over fourteen years ago! The fact is, that suspension was a complete farce. Dozens of players have been known to hurl their bat away in frustration at a poor decision and the fact it hit the square leg umpire was completely irrelevant. The umpire should have been watching more carefully. Which he obviously wasn't doing when he adjudged me out, stumped, a few seconds earlier. When I pressed Crommo he admitted my dropping was not entirely to do with fitness or form, but also the question of team harmony. Apparently I'm seen as a disruptive influence. That really hurt. When I think back on all the damage I've inflicted on the team this tour... the practical jokes alone. Just yesterday I'd shut down an entire motorway with a hoax bomb threat! Swampy stepped in at this point and urged me not to do anything rash.

DAY 72 JULY 23

At 10.15 am (Greenwich Mean Time) I, Warwick Todd, announced my retirement from international cricket — effective immediately. The Australian Cricket Board subsequently released an edited transcript of my retirement speech:

Ladies and gentlemen, Having served Australia for over 12 years with pride and distinction it is with deep regret that I now announce my retirement from international cricket. I would like to thank my friends, family and playing colleagues for the enormous support they have given me over the years. However, I would like to tell the selectors and the Australian Cricket Board to go and get ——.

That's the bit they edited.

At the press conference my retirement was greeted with stunned silence.

Had the press turned up I'm sure there would have been a bigger reaction.

Having dropped this bombshell I returned to my room. As far as I was concerned, if someone wanted to come and talk me out of it my door was open.

DAY 73 | JULY 24

**4th Cornhill Test,
Headingley — Day 1**

Alright then, stuff 'em all! I've had enough of this whole tour. I'm jumping on the first flight home. I can't wait to see the look on Ros' face as I walk through that door a month early.

Warwick and Roslyn Todd today announced the end of their nine-year marriage. In a statement released by a mutual friend, Mr Garry Beckman, it was said Mrs Todd would continue living in the family home and retain custody of the children, Brialanna and Raleisha-May. Mr Todd was unavailable for comment.

First Class Career of
TODD, Warwick Donald

Season	M	Inn	Match Fines	Avrge
1985/86	12	20	$8500	$708.33
1986/87	11	21	$11,750	$1068.10
1987/88	14	25	$13,310	$950.71
1988/89	8	15	$9100	$1137.50
1990/91	10	17	$12,450	$1245
1991/92	11	18	$15,440	$1403.64
1992/93	15	23	$8100	$540
1993/94	10	18	$16,500	$1650
1994/95	12	21	$25,500	$2125
1996/97	9	17	$16,700	$1855.55
Total	112	195	$137,350	$12,683.83